D1189534

SHATTERED DREAMS
The Real Story Behind THE BAY OF PIGS

by
Joe Hill

Copyright © 2005 Joe Hill

All Rights Reserved

ISBN 1-880977-99-0

FIRST EDITION
First printing, April 2005
Second printing, June 2006
Third printing, January 2009

Printed by

Printing Arts Press, Mount Vernon, Ohio

Request for information:

Joe Hill
P.O. Box 32
West Lafayette, OH 43845

E-mail: dad520@sbcglobal.net

This book is based on a true story but some of the names have been changed to protect the individuals.

To my wife Elizabeth, the love of my life, whose dedication to God and our marriage has made my life a joy through the years.

DEDICATION

This story is dedicated to the memory of Marcia Maria Cardona, the bravest and the most adorable little soldier to have served in any army anywhere, and to the men who gave their lives for the cause of freedom from totalitarianism and to save the life of a stranger who had joined their cause and become one of their own.

Thanks to all who helped to put this story together.
A special thank you to Jim Wears for his help,
James J. Isenberg for all the encouragement,
Bill Queen for teaching me to write,
Christine Schrader first and second edits,
Christine Cullison for the third edit,
Pauline Rice for final edit, and proof.

Once I started reading "Shattered Dreams" I was so drawn to it that I could hardly put it down. I think as busy as I am in 3 days I finished it. I guess what drew me was the reality I found in each page. I was especially taken back by Louise and for the cause she fought for.

—*Dave Johnson*

Hi Joe!

I just finished reading your book, "Shattered Dreams". I must say that it was one of the most gripping and riveting accounts I have ever read in my life. What an amazing story! Hollywood couldn't have written a better one.

I will never forget that account. They really should make a movie out of it. I'd be happy to help write a screenplay.

—*Sylvia D'Amato*

The world was on the brink of nuclear war. Castro with the help of the USSR was threatening America with atomic missiles and an army veteran is recruited by the U.S. Government to go to the "Bay of Pigs" and train the rebels to overthrow the Cubans now in power and stop a war. Joe Hill accepts the mission and now tells the real story of what happened and his betrayal, capture and near death. The book "Shattered Dreams" is the story of one man's sacrifice and how his life was forever changed.

—*Bill Queen*
author- *"A Year of Fear"* *"The Escarpment"*
"Valley of the Shadow"

SHATTERED DREAMS

Joe sat staring at the exit sign just above the door, shivering with nerves and from the cold. The old C-47 had taken several hits and was flying with only one engine. He had trained to parachute but had never actually jumped. He still hadn't completely conquered his fear of heights. He figured their altitude was a tad over 11,000 feet. He wondered why they were flying so high. He didn't like it. The higher the plane, the longer he would be exposed to ground fire.

Joe inspected the canvas bag containing the parachute. His heart sank, and he wondered about its safety. The straps were tattered and worn. On further inspection he discovered the metal buckles were so old they were even bent out of shape.

"Did you pack this thing, Lopez?"

"No, Sergeant. I didn't, but I watched them pack it." Lopez smiled knowingly. "Don't worry, it will hold you. Now let's be getting into it. You only have twenty minutes before the jump."

A rope about ten feet long was suspended from Joe's rucksack holding his gear. It would arrive on the ground a split second ahead of him, to reduce the impact of the landing. His carbine was strapped to his body by its rifle sling, along with about thirty pounds of ammo in the front pack. Joe felt the full weight of the combat load when he stood up. The equipment, along with the rest of his gear, weighed nearly eighty pounds.

"Check to make sure all these straps and buckles are fastened tightly." Joe felt trapped under all the weight.

Lopez smiled while he tugged on the straps. "Is okay." Then he took hold of the strap fastened to his own safety harness, hooking it onto a cable that stretched over the exit door of the plane. He then reached over, grabbed the handle of the door, and quickly slid it open. The wind and engine noise came rushing into the plane, along with the smell of burnt gunpowder and smoke. Lopez attached the ripcords of the cargo chutes to the cable and began to push the cases of supplies out the door.

Joe moved slowly toward the opening, his legs starting to go numb from the tight straps of his chute. Stamping his feet, he tried to get some circulation back into his lower limbs. Reaching up, he snapped the hook of his static strap onto the cable before giving it three hard yanks to make sure it was secure. Now he moved to the door and found himself staring out into the emptiness of the night sky. Pitch black except for what appeared to be fireflies darting all about the plane. He wondered what those little lights were. Joe knew they were much too high for lightning bugs. His question was soon answered when one firefly came through the fuselage of the old plane, and with it, the realization that these were tracer bullets from small arms fire. Anti-aircraft shells were bursting all around the crippled plane as it made its last pass over the drop zone.

Joe stood poised in the open door of the old plane, fear sliding her cold fingers around his throat. Although it was cold at this altitude, his hands were sweating as he gripped the edges of the door so tightly that his knuckles turned white. No way I'm jumping out of this plane. I'd have to be crazy, he thought, looking out into the black hole. I'm staying put until this plane lands and nobody is going to tell me any different.

Suddenly, he felt a big foot in the middle of his back. Before he could protest, he felt a shove that thrust him from the plane, sending him out into space just like the cork from a bottle of cheap champagne. Terrified, he clutched at the air while falling helplessly through the dark void. An instant later he felt a tug as the strap tightened enough to pull him into an upright position. That tug should have opened his parachute, but it only pulled the pilot chute part of the way out of its pack. Most people yell 'Geronimo' as they jump, but Joe missed that opportunity. When the static line failed to do its job, he remembered his training, and reached over his shoulder to pull the parachute out by hand. He had already traveled a half-mile, gaining speed with every second in free fall. Joe figured he was traveling about one hundred and twenty miles per hour by now. He could hardly breathe. He hoped he wouldn't pass out. The noise of the wind and the flapping chute only added to his terror. His thoughts ran rampant. Was Louise down there? Would she be the one to find his body?

CHAPTER ONE

Joe Wells shivered as the cold wind cut through his clothing. The wind blew the hard icy flakes downward, stinging his face. It had been snowing off and on all day.

He stopped to light a cigarette and glanced at his watch. It was just a little past two o'clock, only three hours to quitting time. His boss, Brian Mack, always insisted that Joe stick around to help grease and fuel the equipment. That would cost him another hour in the cold. He began to dig through the large pockets of his coat looking for a pair of dry gloves while thinking he sure could use a warmer pair of coveralls. He was really looking forward to quitting time because the winds blowing inland from across Lake Erie were freezing cold and miserable. Although it was only about twenty-five degrees, the driving winds made it feel more like thirty below.

Joe and his boss, whom everyone called Mack, had become fast friends away from the job. At work, however, Joe was just another worker. That's the way it was with them, no favors given and none expected. Looking back towards the construction trailer, he saw his boss coming toward him, moving fast for a man so heavy. But then Mack always moved fast. There were three men behind him almost running to keep up. Mack was waving his hands, and yelling for Joe to shut down. Joe slowed the engine of the big backhoe so he could hear what his boss was saying to him. "Yeah, what's going on?" Joe yelled above the sound of the wind and the idling engine.

"Joe, park that thing. We're calling it a day because these fellows want to talk to you." As Mack talked, he was busy brushing away the melting snow that had began to gather on his balding head.

Joe fired the engine up once again. He watched the wind pick up the black cloud of diesel smoke from the large engine, and carry it quickly away. He then lowered the muddy bucket to the ground so the oiler could grease and refuel it. He placed the gearshift in neutral and let the engine run at an idle for a few moments before shutting it down for the evening. Joe removed the key from the ignition and placed it carefully in the watch pocket of his Levi's. He looked at the three 'suits' standing behind the boss. The shortest of the three men looked familiar. Joe was pretty sure he had never seen the other two men before. Finally, he climbed down off the backhoe, the bulky coveralls covering his slight five-foot seven-inch frame. He removed his cap and ran his fingers through his blond GI brush cut as he walked through the mud to the side work area where Mack stood with the three well-dressed men. Joe broke into a wide grin when he finally recognized the short figure of the older man.

"Well, I'll be," he said. "Colonel Polk, what brings you to this part of Ohio? It can't be just to see one of your old army buddies."

Mack excused himself with a wave. "While you people get acquainted I had better finish closing down the job for the day."

Joe knew he had stretched the word 'buddy' quite a bit when he had first spoken to the older man of the three 'suits'. Their relationship had been much like his association with Mr. Mack. Do your job, and do it right!

"Well, son, as a matter of fact, we have come all this way in this weather just to talk to you. Since you're still in the army reserves, I thought we might be able to do a little business. By the way, it's no longer Colonel. Now it's General with two stars." Grinning as he spoke, the General showed a high dollar set of false teeth.

Joe noticed the teeth because he had been present that night, about five years ago, when the colonel had gotten three of his front teeth knocked out. It had happened in a bar not far from the army-training base at Breckenridge, KY.

"Well congratulations, General. I'm still in the reserves, so I'm still yours to command, sir." Joe grinned, trying not to laugh as he thought about that fight. The only other time he and this man had talked face to face was after that incident. That's when life had become real interesting. He had gotten fourteen weeks of intensive training. But now that was in the past, or at least he hoped so. "I don't know if I should bow or salute," he said with a crooked smile.

"This time a handshake will do, Joe," the old General said with a twinkle in his eye, and a slight smile on his face. "Let me introduce these men from the Department of Justice. They have a small job that needs done. I told them you are just the man they're looking for."

Joe had a feeling he was in big trouble. It flashed through his mind that the general had never spoken this many words to him in all the time he was under his command. However, back then, the General had sergeants to do his talking for him.

The General gestured with his hand, pointing to the taller of the two men. "Joe, this is Richard Bristol and his assistant John Smith. They're with the CIA. They want to talk to you. They'll buy beer for you and the crew, but they'll want to speak with you alone."

The CIA? He had said CIA in such an offhand manner that Joe was taken aback. This was not an organization that most people would mention in such a casual manner.

Smith, being closest to Joe's age, didn't offer a handshake but just gave a slight nod of his head, and stood watching as the general and Bristol talked with Joe.

The strong wind blew Smith's coat open for an instant, allowing a quick glimpse of the handle of a Colt-45 protruding from a shoulder holster before Smith quickly closed and buttoned the coat, fastening only one button. Joe also noticed that Smith never let his hand stray far from the front of his jacket. He was keeping his hand close to the handle of that Colt.

Joe closely watched Smith. He had had to deal with many bullies in his teenage years, and had learned to recognize one at a glance. Smith may have been just a bodyguard for Bristol, but he also might have been there as an intimidation factor. He couldn't decide exactly who the players were until he knew for certain what game they played.

Bristol spoke for the first time. "Call me Richard. I want you to know that we aren't in a hurry. Let's take some time and get to know each other. We can have a nice chat, drink a beer or two, have a little snack and get out of this wretched weather," he said, as he offered his hand to Joe. While they shook hands, he thought Bristol's hand was as formidable as a machine tool.

Joe and the General walked behind Bristol and Smith toward a new dark green 1961 Chrysler New Yorker. The license plate read 'US Government' and had some very low numbers, indicating a high government official. He looked at the plush gray upholstery, hesitating. "Are you sure you want me to get into that car? I've got mud all over me."

"Don't worry about it. The motor pool takes care of my car. They'll clean it when we finish our business. That's one of my privileges," the General said proudly. "Smith and Bristol are driving it back to the post. They'll send someone back with it after it's all cleaned up, and I'm ready to leave. I was thinking I might want to stay behind to talk to you a little bit, Joe, after these fellows go back to the post."

Again there was that little twinkle in the old man's eye. Joe had learned years before that this particular look usually meant trouble for him. Smith and Bristol rode in the front seat, Joe and the general sat in the back. The warm heater and plush interior felt comfortable after working outside in the cold weather. John Smith drove. Joe wondered if that was his real name. He had time to ponder the situation because no one spoke, and Joe took his cue from the rest, and kept his mouth shut. The only sounds that could be heard were the hum of the heater, and the swish of the wiper blades sweeping the snow from the windshield. Joe hoped he could stay awake because the warmth beckoned him to slumber. Although he wanted to ask questions, Joe refrained, waiting for someone else to break the silence.

His crew had always stopped at the 'Red Neck Lounge'. It was close, the beer cheap, and the establishment didn't mind the mud and dirt of the construction workers, but that wasn't where they ended up this evening. Never let it be said that a pipeline worker ever turned down a free drink wherever they were offered one. They pulled into the parking lot of a nightclub. Smith stopped the vehicle, got out, and walked around to the back where he opened the trunk, and removed a small attaché case. He fastened it to his left wrist with a handcuff attached to a twelve-inch chain.

Bristol stepped out of the car, and spoke to Joe. "We told your boss where to bring the crew after they have finished shutting down for the day. Now I have to make a phone call." He walked toward the phone booth in front of the bar.

When they entered the bar it took a few seconds for Joe's eyes to adjust to the dim light after the glare from the snow. Joe quickly scanned the room. He was used to bars where fights were common, and no one was immune to a thrown bottle or a sucker punch.

When they finally sat down at a table, Joe could contain his curiosity no longer.

"General, can you tell me what this is all about?"

10

"I'm afraid I'll have to leave that up to Mr. Bristol," the senior army officer replied. "The only thing I can say is they want you to go to a place much warmer than it is here. While we're waiting, why don't you tell me what happened to that friend of yours? I think his name was Stanley."

Joe smiled. He remembered the night that Stanley had heaved the general over four tables knocking out three of his front teeth. However, the smile quickly faded. "I heard he died last year of a brain tumor, sir."

"You'll soon find out that story isn't true," the general said with a slight smile. "I can't tell you more than this. Stanley Kennedy is alive and well. That was just rumor," he added.

Bristol was still on the phone, and Smith stood talking with the proprietor of the nightclub. Joe's older brother Paul, was the first of the crew to arrive. He came hurrying over to the big corner table where Joe and the general were sitting. "I want to know what is going on, Joe. What do these people want from you?"

Joe looked up at his brother. "Paul, why don't you just sit down and relax. All you need to know for now is that these nice people are buying the drinks. I'll tell you after they tell me, but right now you know as much as I do. Do you remember this man?" Joe indicated the General.

"Yeah," Paul answered. "I remember him from training camp. He was the Colonel in charge at Breckenridge. He's the one who gave you and Stanley all that nice extra training," Paul replied with a smirk. "I've always liked him just for that reason. But who are the other two?" Paul asked, as he stood up, heading for the washroom.

Joe ignored his brother's question. He leaned his head toward the General speaking in a low voice. "I don't know what you want, but you do know Paul will be a problem if this thing is supposed to be any kind of a secret. When he gets a few drinks in him, he can't keep quiet."

The general answered him with just a slight nod of his head, because by now the rest of the crew had started to straggle in. They quickly filled up the table where Joe and the general were sitting. In a loud and boisterous manner, the men grabbed another table and shoved them together. The bartender stood looking on with a scowl of displeasure on his face. The men ignored him and went on scraping chairs across the floor until there were enough seats for them all. They were in a jovial mood. Summer was the busy time for construction workers. Winter was a drag. Most of the men spent the winter months hunkered down in a shabby little motel room, missing their families without even a television to watch. This was promising to be pleasant diversion. No one objected when Smith announced, "Put your money back in your wallet, boys. Your cash is no good tonight." The scraggly looking men cheered, and clapped Smith on the back.

The bartender kept the drinks coming, treating the dirty construction workers like they were kings. He didn't seem to care what they looked like now as long as the money kept pouring into the cash register. For about three hours, the party continued with free booze and steak dinners for the entire crew. They had no idea what this was all about, and they didn't care. They were enjoying the free ride.

Bristol stood, and picked up the glass of gin and tonic he had been nursing most of the evening. He signaled with a slight hand gesture for Joe to accompany him, and they went into a private room at the back of the bar. Obviously, Bristol had made arrangements with the man running the establishment for the use of the room. As he was closing and locking the door, he said, "I know almost everything there is to know about you, that's why I want to talk."

Joe knew Smith would be just outside the door to ensure that they would not be interrupted. Joe didn't want any trouble with Smith or Bristol. Not that he felt afraid; he only agreed to the meeting out of respect for his friend, the general. "Why the locked door?" Joe asked Bristol.

"Don't be difficult," Bristol ordered, the tone of his voice revealing the fact that he wasn't used to having his authority questioned. "I know you don't like locked doors, but privacy is important. I know you will keep to yourself what I'm about to tell you. That's one of the reasons you were chosen for this job. The General told us he would trust you with his life." Bristol glared at him. "Joe, you can't say anything about what I'm about to tell you, not even to your brother. This is classified top-secret, and a matter of National Security. Can I depend on you?"

Joe slowly nodded his head in agreement.

Bristol pushed a form into Joe's hand. "Sign this document. It's a promise that you will keep this interview a secret."

Joe looked at the form letter and saw that just two spaces were blank. Although he was somewhat put off by Bristol's abrupt manner, he filled in the missing service number APF2389328, and signed the document. Joe continued to hold the form as he listened intently while Bristol continued to emphasize the need for them to be secretive.

Joe wanted to laugh. He thought that Bristol was being a bit melodramatic. However, he suppressed the smile that lurked behind a bored expression. Get on with it, he thought.

Bristol paused for a few moments, and then stated, "Now don't interrupt me until I'm finished. Castro has gotten out of hand and we, the CIA, are training a group of people to remove him. This group includes some of his own people that he banished from Cuba." When Bristol placed extra emphasis on the word 'banished', Joe made a mental note of it. Bristol continued to talk and asked Joe several pointed questions. "I have been told you don't speak any Spanish. Is that correct? Are you still physically fit? Could you parachute from a plane? Are you up to date on all your shots, tetanus and so on?" He drilled Joe for about an hour.

Joe threw the paper that he had signed down on the table. "How about me asking a few questions for a change?"

"Go ahead," Bristol said as he leaned back in his chair.

"Why me? How did you come to the conclusion that I could, or would do such a crazy thing? Even if I agree to do it, what makes you think I have the leadership skills to pull it off? If you had asked General Polk, he would have told you I washed out of the Special Forces training because I had problems learning the other languages required. You should also know I'm used to following orders, not giving them. I really don't think I'm the one you want for this mission. I've been off active duty for a long time now, and I don't think I have that edge anymore."

Bristol waved away his objections. "We think you are just the man for the job. We looked at the records of hundreds of candidates. We believe you to be the most qualified, and you are still in the reserves. The construction work seems to have kept you in shape. Besides, Joe, your country needs you. Weren't you trained to do this sort of thing? I never thought you were one of those freeloaders who go into the military, get all of the benefits, and then let someone else do his fighting for him. Are you one of those men, Joe?"

"No, sir." He swallowed his anger. "I'm just a little afraid this job is over my head. Can I think about it for a while? Maybe you can find someone better qualified in the meantime."

Bristol picked up the signed paper. "When you signed the document here on the table, I felt that was pretty much your answer, that you had agreed to do the job. Everything has been explained, and all of your questions have been answered. I need to know before I leave here tonight. You realize I could get orders cut for you in a moment with or without your approval. We would rather have you go willingly. It makes for a more efficient operator," Bristol said grimly. "I would like to give you more time, but time is the one thing we don't have much of. As I said before, your records indicate that you are the best person for this job. A man who would help his country if called upon." Bristol stood, waiting.

"I don't want to lose my job," Joe said, knowing he didn't have that many marketable skills. If he lost his position, he might not find a job when he returned state side. Then what would he do?

Bristol reassured him. "As you know, your employer, Mr. Mack, is part owner of the construction company you work for. He has agreed to hold your job for you while you are gone. If you take on this mission, you will be given a field commission of second lieutenant. You'll make more money than you ever did working construction."

Joe laughed.

"What do you find so amusing?" Bristol demanded.

"I've seen too many second lieutenants to be tempted with a butter bar. I wouldn't be interested in anything less than a first lieutenant."

With a knowing smile, Bristol replied, "I can't say I blame you. You're wising up already. Still, there is only so much I can do. Let me get the General in here. We'll see what he has to say about this." He opened the door and motioned for Smith. He had been watching the door from his seat at the end of the bar. "Get the General," Bristol said. "His man is asking for a bit more than I have been authorized to offer."

Soon General Polk stepped inside the door of the back room, closing it.

Bristol leaned over so they could confer privately. The General nodded his head, giving Joe one of his famous smiles before walking back into the bar to finish his steak and beer.

Bristol walked back over, and sat down across from Joe. "We can pay you as a first lieutenant, but your rank will be sergeant for this job. Is that acceptable? When you return you can decide if you would like to stay in the army as an officer and a gentleman or dig holes like a groundhog for the rest of your life. That will be your decision."

Joe was still vying for more time, but Bristol wasn't buying the delaying tactics.

"No," he said waving aside Joe's reluctance. "I can't allow you to stall any longer. I have already told you this is a top-secret mission, and no one is to be told about it. Even the General hasn't been told anymore then he had to know. He is here only to approve the agreement we are making with you. Joe, keep in mind that any hint of our intentions could jeopardize the lives of some of our best agents, as well as yourself, also the Cuban nationals you will be working with on this operation."

"These support soldiers will be Cubans?" Joe thought about that. "The Cubans speak Spanish, and as you already know I don't speak or understand Spanish."

"We've been working on that problem and we have arranged for you to have an interpreter." Bristol folded his arms, appearing smug.

My objections are drying up faster then a keg of beer at a pipeline worker's picnic, Joe thought. Bristol had an answer for everything. Joe realized he wouldn't be able to talk himself out of this assignment.

Bristol continued, "Your construction company will keep your pay going here and the government will reimburse them their expenses."

It sounded as if the CIA had it all figured out. "The pay sounds good, but why me? What makes you so sure I can do this?" Joe asked.

"You have had the best ranger training in the world. General Polk tells me you're good at this kind of thing. The best he has ever seen. So you see, General Polk believes you can do it. He says he knows you better than you know yourself."

Joe thought about that. "I am afraid the General's confidence may be misplaced. I've never been in combat in my life. What if I can't handle it?"

"Your training and natural ability will give you what it takes. I've read the reports you have accumulated while on active duty. They've proven to me and many others that you are able to take care of yourself," Bristol argued. Then he added, "Are you afraid, Joe?"

"I've never been this apprehensive in my life!" he admitted. "I'm concerned about being able to handle this assignment, whatever it turns out to be."

Bristol chuckled. "Anyone in his right mind is afraid to go into combat. I know I was."

"When you say combat, exactly who will I be in combat against?" Joe asked.

"I can't tell you all the details yet," Bristol said, "but since you know you will be in Cuba, obviously it will be against enemies of the United States."

"Exactly who would that be?" he asked. "I thought we were friends with the freedom fighters there."

"Well, we are, and we aren't," Bristol answered. "Politics change all the time. We were friends with Batista until the United States had a falling out with him because of his high-handed dictatorship. Then we supported Castro, helping him to throw Batista off the island. Then Castro allied himself with Russia, forming a communist government and his record on civil rights became even worse than Batista's. Now we have allied ourselves with the most current bunch of guerrillas in Cuba. We are trying to help them throw Castro and the communists out of their country." He paused momentarily, then continued. "When the General came in a few minutes ago, he told me he is going to be here a day or two. He will try to fill in some of the blanks I have left open about this mission. I can't do it all in one night, and he can only tell you what little he knows. As I said, his knowledge is somewhat limited. You aren't to say anything to him about what we discussed. Just listen to what he has to say, and then I'll fill you in on all the finer details later. I'll ask him to tell you all he knows, but I really think he just wants to talk with an old buddy, so to speak. I'll have your orders cut as soon as I leave here." Bristol then added, "You understand that on the record you are doing this of your own free will. If you ever try to make it sound otherwise, I warn you that would be a big mistake."

"You know something," Joe said, showing a slight smile that didn't quite reach his eyes, "I'm getting a little tired of your veiled threats. I know you are a lot bigger than I am, but if you have looked at my record, like you say you have, you should know two things for sure. First, if I give my word, then I'm committed to keeping it. Second, if you don't act more like the officer and gentleman you are supposed to be, I'm gonna' kick your butt. You got that, Mister Bristol! I'm only warning you because of the respect I have for General Polk."

Bristol remained seated, his eyes darted to the locked door and back to Joe, as if he was contemplating as to whether or not Smith could get to him before too much damage was done to his posterior.

"Cool down, Joe. Save all that for the battlefield. I heard you were a spunky kid and now I'm beginning to believe it." Bristol slowly stood and picked up Joe's signed document, folded it and put it in his pocket. "Okay, we'll do this a little differently than I had originally planned. I'll leave you to enjoy the evening with your friends. Smith and I will be leaving. We have lots of paperwork before our next meeting. As I said, General Polk will be staying over and I'll be seeing you again in a few days. By the way, welcome aboard," Bristol added. "You will be notified as to where and when. Sometime next week we will send a car to take you to the airport."

With that last statement Bristol unlocked the door, and went back into the bar. He gave a hand signal to Smith who, in turn, motioned to the bartender. He handed him a large sum of money.

Bristol turned and waved to the crew. "See that these boys have fun tonight," he told the bartender before he turned, walking out the front door behind Smith.

Joe slid into a small booth away from the others to try to clear his head and recover from the verbal beating he had just received from Bristol. He felt angry, and maybe just a little sorry he had agreed to go. Still, from the way Bristol had talked, it seemed apparent that he really didn't have a choice in the matter. They just wanted him to think he volunteered so he would be a more cooperative agent. Wasn't that what Bristol had insinuated? Joe was still in the reserves and thus under the finger of Uncle Sam.

He felt a hand on his shoulder and looked up into General Polk's face. He sat down across from Joe. "Did you recommend me for this mission because you think I'm the best man for the job or as a way to get even with me?" he asked.

The General ignored his question. "We'll be spending a little time with each other for the next couple of days so how about you dropping this general stuff and just call me Alex."

"You didn't answer my question."

"Joe…. I do believe you are the best man for this operation. You are well trained. Moreover, the nature of your job keeps you on the road, away from family and friends for long periods of time." Alex changed the subject. "Why would you think that I selected you because I wanted to get even?"

"Don't you remember when my friend Stan threw you over those tables and knocked out a few of your teeth?"

Polk started to laugh, "How could I ever forget that? It was my own fault. I shouldn't have said anything when I was out of uniform. I learned an important lesson that evening. Don't stick your nose into business that doesn't concern you. I was out of uniform; therefore, I got treated like one of the boys, so enough of that." He dismissed the revenge theory.

"Joe, I kept an eye on you all through boot camp, and watched how you managed to help Stanley with his learning disability. We were going to kick him out of the military until he began responding to your leadership. I waited to see what you could do with him. You didn't disappoint me one bit. You see, I knew who you were, and the sergeant who picked you up awhile before that incident was one of mine. I wasn't in that bar by accident. It's just that I went a step too far by intervening when I was out of uniform."

"You mean the crazy sergeant with the screaming eagle patch who drove us to town was one of your men?" Joe asked.

"He sure was," the General answered. "I wanted to know where you were going, and how you behaved when you were away from camp. You did just fine, aggressive, but not foolish. Stanley didn't fare quite as well when he overreacted to minor criticism."

"Then you purposely provoked the fight?" For once, Joe was surprised.

"Not exactly, but the way things turned out, I found out what I wanted to know about you the hard way."

"So now what?" Joe asked.

"Let's go back and finish our refreshments. Since I am staying over, tomorrow we can go to the hockey game in Cleveland. How does that sound?"

"Fine with me," Joe answered, as he got to his feet. "But Mack won't be very happy with me. He will need another operator for the backhoe."

Scooting back his chair, the General said. "Sit back down. I'll go speak to Mack." Alex walked away, soon returning with Mack in tow.

"I have your replacement coming, but he can't be here until Thursday. Nevertheless, you can take off at noon tomorrow. That way we won't lose any time. You can work in the morning, and get us caught up for the day," Mack said.

It seemed they had everything worked out. Joe liked the idea of only working a half-day. "Okay, Alex, I'll see you around noon tomorrow."

The next afternoon Joe was in for a pleasant surprise. He enjoyed being with Alex. The older man seemed pleasant, and he found that under all the brass, there was a very nice man. After the game they went to a restaurant to have dinner.

"Joe, your contact for this mission will pick you up on the job day after tomorrow. You should have your bag packed, ready to go."

"Will Mr. Smith be the one who picks me up for the ride to the airport?"

Alex shook his head. "No. We want you to just report to work as usual. The man will find you. I've been told to tell you that he will drive up and ask for you by name; then he will place his hands behind his head stretching like he is tired."

Joe laughed. This was just so cloak and dagger "Why all this foolishness? You can't be serious." Joe looked around trying to spot some hidden cameras. "This is beginning to sound terribly corny."

"Well that's the way the spooks want it," Alex said, using military slang for the Central Intelligence Agency. "So I guess for now we'll have to play their little game."

Early Friday morning, a red Corvette Stingray drove onto the construction site where Joe was working. The automobile pulled up to the curb, and sat there with the engine running. The driver stayed in the car staring at Joe and Mack, who were standing by the curb.

Finally, the man rolled down his window and gave a small wave. "Hi fellows. My name is Bill Scott. I was told I could find Joe Wells here." With that said, the man placed his hands behind his head and stretched as if he were trying to relax.

"You found him. What can I do for you?"

"I need to speak with you for a minute. Get in the car, will you? Let's go for a ride. Where is your duffel?" Scott asked, the use of the word duffel marking him as a military man, "We'll have to get going. You don't have much time to make your flight. The plane leaves at 0730."

Mack walked over to the automobile. "Joe, take care of yourself. I don't know what's going on, but I feel uneasy about all this secrecy."

Joe hesitated. "I sure don't like leaving you in a fix like this. What happened to my replacement? Wasn't he supposed to be here this morning?"

"No problem there; the guy's in town. He called me last night. I told him to report for work this afternoon. I was hoping you wouldn't have to go," Mack said, clapping Joe affectionately on the back as Joe placed his one small suitcase in the trunk of the Corvette.

"Just settle back and enjoy the ride," Scott said. "I'll get you there in time for lift off."

They arrived at Wright-Patterson Air Force Base in Dayton, Ohio, just in time to see the pilot start the engine of the large cargo plane. Its propellers were loud as they whirled and spun.

Joe had so many questions buzzing around in his head, that it was making him feel a little dizzy. "Where am I going?" he asked Scott as he retrieved the duffel bag from the trunk. "Will you be going with me?"

"I can only tell you this. The flight you are about to miss if you don't hurry, is going to the Homestead Air Force Base in Florida. And no, I won't be going with you," Scott said. "I have a hot date tonight." He winked and waved as he pulled away from the curb. The sound of squealing tires, and the smell of burnt rubber were the last memories Joe had of his transport acquaintance.

Joe hurried aboard the cargo plane just in time for the take off. He felt he had just turned a new chapter in his life, and wondered what effect this would have on his future.

CHAPTER TWO

On the plane, Joe found a box to sit on along the wall. This was not a passenger plane, but Joe had been on these old C-47s before. He had been on enough of them to know how to make himself as comfortable as possible. He stayed out of the way of the four-man crew. It proved to be an easy task because they went about their duties, completely ignoring Joe the whole time they were in the air.

The over-loaded plane had struggled to lift off. The ancient ship lived up to its reputation as a gooney bird. As they lifted to flight altitude, the aircraft encountered strong head winds. The wings began shaking and groaning with every forward movement.

With three stops scheduled before reaching their destination, it would take almost seven hours to make the short flight from Ohio to Florida. Joe sat back watching with interest as the men inspected the skin of the old plane. Apparently, some of the rivets had worked themselves loose so the crewmen were drawing circles around the areas with a bright yellow grease pencil.

Joe soon lost interest, leaned back, and closed his eyes. He thought about the training he had received in the army the first time he served Uncle Sam in active service. He knew it was the best the military had to offer at the time, but he had doubts about the training being up to date enough to keep him and his team alive now.

He mentally pushed the worry aside, and seeking a diversion, he thought back to his first stint in the service. He had teamed up with a 250 pound six-foot four street fighter named Stanley. It seemed an unlikely match because Joe stood five-foot seven-inches and weighed 140 pounds when he had a rifle slung over his shoulder. Sometimes it embarrassed him to be seen with Stanley. He heard that some of the men referred to them as "Laurel and Hardy" behind their backs. Still, they became best friends and managed to get into a lot of trouble together.

He most remembered an incident that happened when he and Stanley got their first off the base leave from boot camp. They decided to go to a popular bar near Breckenridge, Kentucky, to drink and meet some girls. They were having a great time until his boot camp friend, Stanley, said, "It's hot in this place!" His face had turned a bright shade of red with beads of sweat dampening his forehead and running down his face. His shirt hung wet in back where perspiration trickled down between his shoulder blades.

"Too much beer?" Joe asked, while pulling at the knot in his own tie, which seemed to be strangling him. He loosened it a bit.

Stanley reached up and loosened his necktie. "Whew, that's better."

"Hey, you! Soldiers!" An older man called out to them from across the room. "Straighten those ties back up and act like soldiers."

Stanley looked at Joe and just for spite took his tie completely off. Half-drunk, he staggered as he walked. "Hey Joe, let's show that old man we don't have to listen to him. We don't have to pay attention to that old fogy."

"Stanley," Joe warned. "We don't want trouble with the townspeople."

Stanley directed his voice towards the old man saying, "You can't do nothing to us. Did you hear what I said, old man? We don't have to do what you say."

Joe wasn't sure what was going on so he left his tie around his neck. Stanley was a little slow upstairs sometimes, but he usually listened to Joe. However, this time the booze had full control. He pushed Joe aside, and Joe's words bounced off Stanley like a feather trying to make a dent in a rock.

"I just wonder who he thinks he is," Stanley continued, on a roll. "What we do or how we dress is none of his business. He ain't our boss. He can't tell us what to do."

The older man stood up to get a better view of the two soldiers. He stomped over to their table. "Put that tie back on soldier," he ordered. "You men are a disgrace to the uniform. You should be taught a lesson on how to conduct yourselves in public."

The other patrons had noticed the disturbance. They were laughing and enjoying the show. A fat man sitting at a table called out, "Watch out soldier boys, daddy's getting angry!" One of the women at the table was hanging onto his arm, laughing, and egging him on.

"You tell 'em, Honey," she shrieked.

Joe and Stanley watched as the older man's face twisted into a scowl, as he neared their table. They could even see the veins standing out on

Sign at Main Gate, Camp Breckinridge, Morganfield, Kentucky.
(photo from 1955)

his neck and forehead. He started to reach into his back pocket. "Do you know who I am?" he snorted.

"Look out!" Stanley shouted above the din. "He's going for a knife!" In a split second Stanley grabbed the grouchy gentleman by the back of the neck and one leg, and lifted him high above his head. With a heaving motion he threw the old fellow through the air like a rag doll. The old man made two or three revolutions before landing with a resounding crash, right onto a table where some of the hecklers were sitting. The impact turned the table over sending its occupants scattering in all directions. Food and drinks sprayed the floor, along with the old man. He floundered around on the deck like a freshly caught fish, slipping and sliding in the barbecue sauce, beer, and potato salad. When he managed to get to his feet, he was covered from head to toe with sticky red sauce and had a lone French fry clinging to his cheek. He straightened up and began wiping beer and cigarette butts from his face.

"You fools. You don't know who I am. Do you?" He started yelling in a high, authoritative voice, "MPs. MPs!" Blood oozed from a cut on his cheek and his mouth was bleeding. He pulled out a handkerchief and dabbed at his lips, spitting blood onto the floor.

The people sitting at the table had apparently lost their appetite, and their sense of humor because they went running for the door. That effectively ended the heckling.

"Why did you do such a crazy thing like that, Stan?" Joe yelled at his friend above the noise and the uproar.

"He was going for a knife," Stanley said. "It was self defense."

"Well, this time you've defended us right into the guard house," Joe hollered at his oversized friend. "He wasn't going for a knife. He was reaching for his billfold. Now just look at what you've done! We'll be lucky if we don't go to the stockade. You know better than to do stuff like this. I don't know who that dude is, but I'll bet you a month's pay that he is not a civilian. Come on, let's get out of here!"

Stanley threw back his head and laughed a little insanely, not saying a word. Joe saw the angry look in the bouncer's eyes and he grabbed Stanley by the arm, pulling him forcefully out of the back door, into the alley.

Joe decided discretion was much better than futile explanations, so he had to find a way of escape. Looking around in the alley, he found a large trashcan that contained one bag. Quickly, Joe dumped the trash out on the ground and climbed in. Stanley never slowed or looked for a place to hide. The only thing on his mind was flight and his footsteps faded down the alley as Joe pulled a lid over his head and waited for it to get dark. The trashcan reeked of the smell of rotten fish and spoiled eggs. He held his nose, and breathing through his mouth, he tried to resist the urge to gag. He knew if he started gagging he would upchuck and lose it all. Surely someone would hear and it would be all over for him.

After what seemed like hours, it began to get dark. The eerie silence gave him courage to creep out of the can. His limbs felt cramped, and he silently promised himself that he would never find himself in that type of predicament again. Joe quietly walked down the alley, looking over his shoulder. The night around him hung like a silken garment. A stray cat, attracted by the smell of rotten fish, began to follow Joe, but made a hasty retreat when he heaved an empty beer can in its direction. He mentally grumbled and berated himself while he walked the thirty miles back to camp. A couple of cars stopped to offer him a ride, but changed their minds as soon as they got a whiff of him.

Main entrance to Camp Breckinridge, Morganfield, Kentucky. (photo from 1955)

Arriving back at the barracks close to 0500 Saturday morning, Joe hobbled up the steps on his aching feet. Stanley had managed to catch a ride back, and had waited several hours for Joe. Scared that something had happened to his buddy, he had started throwing his belongings into one large duffel bag. Stanley looked relieved when he saw Joe stumble into the barracks.

He threw himself down on his cot, and leaned on one elbow. He noticed the change in Stan. Now he looked tired, and the fight had gone out of him. Stanley started to blubber in fear and excitement. He stuttered, "They ran after me just about all night, but they never did catch me. I finally lost the cops and caught a ride back." He stopped, a puzzled look passing over his features. "I don't know who that old man was. That little squabble with him sure caused one heck of a fuss."

"I don't know who he was either, and I hope we never find out," Joe said. "It'll be okay, Stan. That old guy didn't get a good look at us. You know the light in that place wasn't all that bright. Now, what are you doing with that duffel bag and all your gear?"

"I'm leaving. I'm gonna get out of here before I get you or me or anyone else in a bunch of trouble. You never done nothin wrong, so nobody can blame you for what happened. If I'm not around any more, maybe they'll just forget the whole thing. I've been thinking all night, and I got it figured out. You would be better off if you didn't have a friend like me."

Joe smiled. It touched him that Stanley cared so much about his welfare that he would contemplate going AWOL, but knew that would be the end of Stanley's career in the service, just when he was beginning to show promise of becoming a very good soldier. He sat up on the bunk. "Running away is not a solution, nor is it an option. Unpack your bag and settle down. No one knows who we are in town; besides, they will forget about it in ten or fifteen years." Joe smiled. Stanley was too flustered to see any humor in the situation. Joe walked over to pull clothing and shaving gear out of the bag, placing them back in the footlocker. "You are staying put. You're my best friend. I would be all alone if you left," he reasoned.

The friendship speech got through to the giant of a man and he visibly relaxed and started to laugh. Joe wasn't always sure what Stanley was laughing at. The man would often start laughing at the most inopportune times. Still, because of his size and mental deficiencies, few men laughed at him. Or, at least they pretended to laugh with him.

"What if that guy is some bigwig?"

Busy pulling his clothing off so he could get into bed, Joe stopped to look at Stanley. "You mean the guy in the bar?"

Rifle range, Camp Breckinridge, Morganfield, Kentucky. (photo from 1955)

Interior of one of the barracks, Camp Breckinridge, Morganfield, Kentucky. (photo from 1955)

"Yeah. Then what?" Stanley stood transfixed in the semi-darkness of the room.

Joe got down to his skivvies and jumped into bed. "They don't know us. You worry too much. Go to sleep." He punched his pillow. He barely heard Stanley undressing.

Exhausted, they fell asleep.

Monday morning the barracks came alive at 0200 hours with First Sergeant Mills screaming at the top of his voice, "Wake up! Do you plan to sleep all day? This ain't no motel. Your mommas ain't fixing you pancakes for breakfast! You've had all weekend to get your beauty sleep. We're having a surprise inspection, so fall in with your boots shined, and I do mean shined! Class-A uniform, clean, and pressed. You had better look sharp or your worthless carcass will be standing tall before the Man."

Stanley looked over at Joe as they rushed to ready themselves for the inspection, saying, "I wonder who the Man is. Do you think they are still hunting for us?" Fear filled his eyes as he started to sweat. "We're in big trouble. I just know it. I should have gone AWOL when I wanted to. Maybe you should have gone with me."

For once, Joe thought that his friend might be right but he didn't want to admit it. However, the more that he thought about it, the more he thought Stanley was paranoid. "Just be cool. No one is looking for us. They got us up early for an inspection. You have to expect that when you're in the army."

It took about half an hour to get ready. Finally, they marched outside.

A jeep sped by heading to A Company. The brass would start the long and tedious inspection there. It would be hours before they got back to I Company. Joe watched the jeep go by. His heart started pounding when he saw the colonel in the front seat beside the driver.

"That...That... looked like the guy in the bar. The one I threw across the table," Stanley whispered, standing next to Joe.

Joe blinked several times. It couldn't be. Now we're both being paranoid, he thought, yet he had his misgivings. He stood at ease in the blazing sun and began to sweat. It would be awhile before the big wigs got to their company. There were hundreds of men being inspected. Even if by some coincidence it was the man in the bar, he couldn't possibly identify them or pick them out of such a large lineup. Still....

They were well down the line in I (short for Item) Company. Joe watched the military brass approaching. He saw a colonel with Captain Hays, the company commander. Finally, he got a good look at the colonel's face. He let out a sigh, and his shoulders sagged.

Stanley saw the colonel too. He drew in his breath. "It's him!" he whispered out of the side of his mouth so Joe could hear him. "It's that old guy from the bar. I told you we should have run." Stanley's face

Post Hospital, Camp Breckinridge, Morganfield, Kentucky. (photo from 1955)

Military police checking station, Camp Breckinridge, Morganfield, Kentucky. (photo from 1955)

turned a chalky shade of white. "Let's run, Joe."

"No!" Joe whispered. "Just stand still. Maybe he won't recognize us, it was dark in the bar," Joe reminded his friend.

"Attention!" the company commander ordered. The company stood tall, looking straight ahead. The colonel and the captain with their lower ranking officers moved slowly through the ranks. When they came nearer to them, Joe whispered to Stanley, "I sure hope they don't hear my knees knocking together." He glanced at Stanley and saw that the big, street fighter's face had turned from white to a pasty green color. He thought Stanley looked as if he might faint. Joe licked his dry lips.

Without moving his head, Stanley turned his eyes toward Joe, whispering, "Do they still have a firing squad in the army?"

"I...I don't think so," Joe said, barely moving his lips. "Just be quiet. Don't talk, you're going to give us away. Don't do anything that will draw attention to us!"

Joe felt pure panic when the old colonel stopped in front of him and grabbed the M-1 Garand rifle from his hand. Keeping his eyes straight to the front, Joe could see the man had a badly swollen upper lip, as the old colonel began the usual questions.

"Name, rank and service number, soldier."

"Private Joe Wells, Sir!" he shouted. "Private US Army, 289328, Sir!"

The colonel held the weapon up to the sun, and squinted into the barrel, looking for a speck of dust or any other thing that might help him gig a soldier, but there was nothing in the rifle. He returned the weapon to Joe. Then the swollen lip curled into a crooked little smile and a strange little twinkle danced in the colonel's eyes, as if he and Joe were privy to a secret just between the two of them. Joe's heart pounded so loud he heard it in his ears. He almost let out a loud sigh of relief when the captain and the old colonel continued down the ranks. Pausing for a moment in front of Stanley, he just stood there glaring at the wide-eyed soldier. Stanley took one look at the colonel and fell forward, passing out at the old man's feet.

"Captain, we had better get these men out of the sun. They're starting to fall out," the colonel said.

The colonel and captain conversed in low tones for a moment, the commander busily writing on his clipboard, and then they continued moving on down the ranks. The inspection completed, Captain Hays turned the company over to the first sergeant. "You bunch of sissies fall out for chow, but be back here in formation at 1300 hours."

Joe and Stanley jumped up and down, slapping each other on the back. "I told you the old guy would see so many faces that he wouldn't recognize us. We're home free. He's not going to punish us," Joe said. It felt good to be off the hook. Stanley even looked as if he might survive.

Stanley laughed. "I can't believe we made it, but he sure didn't act like he recognized us." They felt good about fooling the old man, and relieved that there would be no retribution.

However, the next morning, Second Lieutenant Johnston, their platoon leader awakened them at 0200 hours. "Get up sleeping beauties. I can't imagine whom you know to get this assignment. Sergeant Meeker had been trying to sign up with that unit for three years. He was finally accepted just last week."

Joe rubbed the sleep from his eyes. "What are you talking about?"

"You'll find out soon enough," the officer growled. "Get your gear together, and report to Captain Hays."

Joe and Stanley cleaned out their footlockers, stuffing their gear into their duffel bags before they ran up to the duty hut.

The captain stood waiting for them. "Good morning, men. You sure must have made a good impression on the colonel. He requested that

One of the Fine Guest Houses, Camp Breckinridge, Morganfield, Kentucky. (photo from 1955)

you both get a little special training. Any man in this brigade would do just about anything to pull duty with that unit. You have been chosen to represent our company, so don't let us down."

"What unit are you talking about, Sir?" Joe expected the worst.

"You two have been assigned temporary duty with the 101st Airborne Pathfinder Platoons. Report to Lieutenant Smith," Captain Hays said. "You'll catch him at their headquarters. It's only three miles, but you'll have to hurry. You have a half hour, so get moving!"

Stanley and Joe started to double time, their duffel bags slung over a shoulder, and their weapons at port arms. After about two miles, Stanley panted, his breathing loud and labored, "I knew it. He's getting even with us. I told you he would."

Joe continued running. They had to report before the platoon left them behind. "Now, Stanley, it can't be all that bad. Just hang in there, we'll make it through this."

The two privates found Lieutenant Smith writing reports in the duty hut.

They lifted their hands in a salute. "Privates Wells and Kennedy reporting as ordered, Sir," they said in unison as they stood at attention.

The skinny, blond Lieutenant continued writing. He didn't return their salute or acknowledge them, but just let them stand there at attention. Suddenly he looked up and scowled at them, then grudgingly returned their salute.

"You two get out of my office. I'll talk to you outside. Don't ever come in here again without being ordered to do so! Do you understand?"

Joe and Stanley looked at each other and shrugged their shoulders. They walked back outside. "Welcome to the 101st Airborne," Joe said sarcastically.

They watched as a group of men went running by with full packs and weapons at high port. Sergeant Meeker, their sergeant from basic training, ran alongside the men screaming at the top of his lungs with every step. "Your left, left, left, right, left. Pick it up, ladies! Left, right, left, you run like a bunch of Girl Scouts! Grandma was slow, but then she was old. You bunch of sissies had better quit straggling or I'll have you all duck walking your carcass all the way to the training area. Your left, left, left, right, left."

Joe looked over at Stanley and laughed. "I'm sure glad we don't belong to that outfit. They look like they are in for a hard time. I don't envy those guys." Joe watched in amusement as the men receded in the distance.

The Lieutenant came striding out of his office. "Are you two pansies still here? Your platoon just went down the road. You'd better get moving if you hope to catch up with them. Sergeant Meeker doesn't like stragglers; so don't stand there with your mouths hanging open. Pick up your 'TA21' and move out! Hut! Hut! Hut! They are only about a mile ahead of you so you can catch them easily."

"Let's go, Stanley." Joe looked down the road for the platoon. They were out of sight. "Pick up your gear, it's time to hit the road."

"I knew this would happen," Stanley protested. "We'll regret ever coming here. Why, oh why, didn't you let me go AWOL? We could have been in Canada by now."

"You wouldn't like Canada. They drive on the wrong side of the road. Besides, it gets real cold up there, and they talk funny," Joe said ironically. He then lifted his rifle onto his shoulder. "Let's go!" he yelled. With their packs on their backs, their duffel bags in their arms, and their rifles slung over their shoulders, they began to run. Sometime about midmorning they caught up with the unit that had passed them earlier.

The NCO-IC (Non-Commissioned Officer In Charge) Sergeant Meeker was watching for them, and he unloaded on them with both barrels. "What are you doing here, Privates? I remember you from basic and I haven't forgotten that 'squeaker' name you guys stuck me with. What are you doing here? Every one of these guys was at the top of his class and still had a hard time getting into this unit. I don't know who you people know or who you bribed to get in this outfit, but you obviously don't belong here."

"We were ordered to report to you, Sergeant. We don't like it any more then you do."

Joe returned the Sergeant's glare.

"Oh...! So, this unit ain't good enough for you! Aye?" he said in a low voice. Then shifting to a higher octave, he yelled, "Hear this and hear it good! I don't want a bunch of screw-ups, and you two have been screw-ups from the beginning! You wouldn't make a pimple on a ranger's backside! Now drop to the ground and give me fifty."

"Now?" Joe asked. The sergeant got right in Joe's face so close he could smell the stale whiskey on the sergeant's breath. "Yes, now! Do you need a hearing aid? Drop and do fifty, and I mean right now!"

Joe and Stanley dropped to the ground, and grunted out fifty push-ups with a full pack on their backs. Pain ripped through Joe's shoulders and neck. He could barely lift his body on the last push-up, and collapsed face down in the dust. The dirt tasted as bad as it smelled. He turned his head, and spit. He felt a foot pushing into his side.

"IM TIRED OF BABY SITTING YOU TWO...NOW...get into formation, and don't let me catch you falling behind again. As for the rest of you men, because these two wilting violets couldn't keep up, you'll all have to make up for their shortcomings. No more breaks for the rest of this day, and you can thank your new friends for that. You understand that waiting for them has made us all late, so we've missed noon chow. I want all of you to make them feel real welcome...if you get my drift. Break is over. Now saddle up, and move out."

The men groaned and would have been more abusive except they were exhausted, and hitting a man would expend too much energy. "Welcome to the One Hundred and First Airborne Division," someone grunted. "As you have already learned, if one person in this unit makes a mistake, the whole unit pays. So watch your step."

Exhausted at the end of the long day, Joe and Stanley put up their tent. They were ready to lie down when Sergeant Meeker came to visit them.

"You'll be on guard duty tonight so take your tent down and stow it. You won't need it tonight since we will be moving out at 0200. You will be so kind as to wake me at 0100."

"I don't think we can make it another day without sleep, Sergeant." Joe's eyes drooped from sleep deprivation and exhaustion. He thought he might fall asleep standing up.

"So, you're telling me that you guys aren't men enough to pull guard duty. I'm so glad to hear that. If you don't have the guts to make it in this platoon, then I'll be rid of you. Nevertheless, tonight you will stand guard or be sent back to your unit." He poked Joe in the chest with two fingers to make a point. "If you can't pull your own weight around here then the other men will be better off without you." The Sergeant lowered his voice. "Do I make myself clear? Now get out of my face, and you had better not screw-up this time! You two eight balls caused these men to lose out on their breaks, so you will secure the camp while the rest of the men catch up on their sleep."

"I am so tired I can hardly stand up," Stanley protested.

"Oh no, the new men need a nappy," the NCO said sarcastically. "These poor babies are tired and need their beauty sleep." Then he yelled, "I don't want to hear your bellyaching! GET OUT OF HERE, AND TO YOUR POSTS NOW!"

Embarrassed to be chewed out in front of the rest of the platoon, they quickly packed up the tent. Some of the men laughed, while others taunted them. "Poor, pitiful babies."

Joe straightened up, throwing his shoulders back. "Let's show them, Stanley. We can take all they dish out, and come back for more. We're real men. Lets show them we can do it."

"Okay, Joe. I'll do the best I can," Stanley said. They ran to their post to stand guard.

The training was grueling. Joe and Stan soon found out that the Cadre came down hard on slackers, and the other men knew how to get even with a team member who made mistakes, so they worked extra hard to keep pace. Joe also found out that in the army one has little time to himself. Busy soldiers are happy soldiers seemed to be the theme. When they weren't training, they had to clean the barracks. The dormitories were built in the forties to house infantrymen before they were sent to fight in Europe. The buildings were originally built as temporary shelters constructed of rough sawed lumber. They still had the bare wood floors.

"Let's all have a 'GI' party," the squad leader announced, amid the groans and cursing of the men. "Shut up and have fun!"

"Joe. We're going to have a party. What are we celebrating?" Stanley asked, looking expectantly at his buddy.

The GIs laughed. "What's the joke?" Joe looked at the leader, feeling apprehensive. He had been in the army long enough to be skeptical. Most things were not as they seemed on the surface. "What's up?" Joe asked again, watching his comrades fill buckets with water. Some held their helmets upside down under the faucet, filling them to the brim. Someone threw a wet sponge at Joe, and it hit his shirt, making a wet spot before it landed on the wooden floor in front of his feet.

A wet rag was hurled through the air, and slapped Stanley full in the face. He grabbed the offending rag, and snarled, holding it in his big hand, trying to figure out who had thrown it at him.

The men got down on their knees, and began scrubbing the rough wooden planks that made up the flooring. Joe reached out, and put a restraining hand on Stanley's shoulder. "Come on, friend. Let's join the party." He got down on his knees, and began to scrub with the sponge. It soon became evident that the sponge would not last long. The old wooden floor was splintered, and he had to be careful that he didn't run a splinter under his fingernails.

This wasn't his idea of a party. He got a scrub bucket to rinse out the sponge. Stanley did the same with his rag. The water had turned black and was changed so many times that Joe lost count. So this was what they meant when they referred to a 'GI' party. Joe hoped that the next time they had one he wouldn't get invited.

"Be sure to clean between the cracks of the wooden planks," someone said above him.

He didn't look up, but concentrated instead on cleaning the ancient floor without getting wounded. He didn't want to receive a Purple Heart for getting a splinter. That made him laugh. Stanley looked his way, but Joe shook his head and kept on scrubbing.

Later, Joe and Stanley were ordered up to the second level. The floors there were no better than the rough floors on the first floor. At least they were working alone, and didn't have the squad leader breathing down their backsides. Joe looked up to see Stanley cleaning in front of him. He slopped his sponge in the inky water, and gave the sponge a flip, splattering water all over Stanley's back.

His giant of a friend looked back at him. He laughed. He stood up, and threw water at Joe. Ready for the attack, Joe jumped out of the way. That spurred Stanley to more action. Laughing, Joe started down the steps with Stanley in hot pursuit. Stanley picked up the bucket of dirty water, and ran after Joe. Their footsteps on the bare wooden floors sounded like thunder rolling downstairs.

Lieutenant Smith came to see what all the commotion was about. Just as the officer mounted the steps, Stanley threw the bucket of filthy mop water. The soapy black water hit Joe in the back of the head and the Lieutenant caught it full in the face.

"Sorry, Sir!" Joe straightened up, saluted, the wet sponge still in his hand. The dirty water ran down Joe's face and off onto his shirt in dirty streaks. "We didn't know you were there, Sir!" Lieutenant Smith's face turned the color of a ripe plum under the soapsuds. He was shaking with anger while the water ran down his face and dribbled off his chin, leaving a wet streak down the front of his shirt, and trousers.

"You both will pay for this with a few extra duties," the lieutenant howled, as he shook the water out of his hair like a wet dog. "Report to the company commander's office in the morning at 0200 hours. We'll see how you two like hanging off a garbage truck for a day or two."

Poor Stanley stood there looking like a sheep dog. He always managed to get Joe into trouble and worried that he would one day do something to end the friendship, but that never happened.

CHAPTER THREE

"You had better get your things together. We're approaching the airport," one of the crewman on the plane told Joe, bringing him out of his reverie and into the present time.

The plane landed on the runway of the Homestead Air Base at 5:30 P.M. or 1730 hours military time, March 12th, 1961. He waited until most of the crew left the plane and watched the fuel truck move up alongside the aircraft. Joe sure wasn't looking forward to his meeting with that government man. As he dismounted the steps, a man in a disheveled uniform greeted him.

For an airman first class, this man didn't make a very good first impression. He looked like a man who had little pride in himself or his unit. Joe wondered if the general had kept him from turning out like this man. The short, heavy-set man looked as if he had had a rough day. Still he smiled, revealing yellow teeth, that is, those that weren't broken or missing. Joe couldn't help but think that he could have his teeth fixed at government expense, if he wanted to. One of the Air Force's benefits was free medical care; however, the red tape could be more than some men wanted to tackle. Still, he thought the man should make an effort. Joe almost stepped back when he smelled the strong garlic on his breath. The man perspired heavily in the southern Florida sunshine.

"Hi, fellow, my name is Jack," he said, while extending a greasy hand. Jack pumped Joe's hand up and down, leaving the palm of his hand a greasy mess. He motioned him to get into his jeep, and before he could sit down, Jack popped the clutch, and the little beast leapt forward. Joe fell back into the seat, grabbing the sides of the canvas-covered seat, trying to hold on. Jack drove down an access road that ran parallel along the runway, the vehicle rocking and bumping along the pot-marked road.

It seemed to Joe that the driver swerved back and forth trying to hit every pothole and rock he could find. Joe couldn't help but laugh as the little vehicle lurched back and forth down the road, leaving a cloud of exhaust smoke and dust behind them.

Jack chattered all the way from the airstrip about the weather, and gave his opinion on how hard it was to keep these old crates flying. Jack didn't seem to need any input, so Joe sat quietly, letting his talkative driver ramble on. Shortly, they pulled up in front of a large Quonset hut about a mile from the airport.

"Here you are." Jack sat back on the seat, pointing to the structure. "Go through the first door and you'll find the office on the right. Go on in and make yourself at home."

"Who am I waiting for?" Joe asked.

"I don't know," Jack replied. "My orders were to transport you to this building and leave you here." He shifted the jeep into gear and took off in a cloud of dust.

Joe quickly walked into the building to get out of the blazing sunshine. The inside of the building felt cool. He had to squint his eyes because the interior of the building seemed dark after coming in out of the bright sunlight. Joe's eyes adjusted, and he located the office where he had been directed. After knocking on the door, and getting no response, he walked on up the hall where the tap of a typewriter broke the silence. Joe opened the office door to see a middle aged blond woman sitting behind a battered old gray desk. Her fingers danced across the typewriter keys. There were make-up stains on her collar, and some ink splotches on the sleeves and the front of her white blouse. Her make-up appeared too thick, and looked a few shades too dark for her light complexion. She looked up, smiling at Joe.

"Hello. I'm Sergeant Joe Wells...I was told to report to the office next door, but no one seems to be there. Would you know anything about it?"

"I'm Joyce. I was told to expect you. Give me about five minutes to finish this report, then I'll be right with you. You may wait in the office down the hall. I was instructed to send you there. Oh, by the way Sergeant Wells, you'll find some uniforms in there. I was told to tell you to get into a clean uniform ASAP. Mr. Bristol is bringing someone to meet you, and he said it's important that you meet them in your Class-A uniform," Joyce said before returning to her typing, her fingers flying over the keys once again.

Joe considered himself dismissed. He walked down the hall, and turned the knob. The door was unlocked so Joe walked inside. He paused just inside the doorway, his eyes quickly sweeping the room, finding it empty except for a large gray metal desk, and six chairs upholstered with leather. In the one window high overhead an undersized air conditioner rattled noisily, but wasn't doing a very good job of cooling the room. A large fan set behind the desk. Joe noticed a door at the back of the room, and assumed it would be a closet or storage space. He walked back, and opened the closet door. Inside were one Class-A uniform and two sets of army fatigues, freshly cleaned and pressed, hanging neatly on hangers. On the floor there was a pair of low quarters, and two pairs of jump boots.

Hurriedly, Joe took off his travel-wrinkled uniform and put on the fresh one. He was relieved to discover that the uniform almost fit him. It had the screaming eagle patch of the 101st Airborne sewn on the sleeve, master sergeant stripes and enough hash marks to make it appear that he had been in the army for a very long time. He had just finished pulling on his trousers when a tap resounded on the heavy walnut stained door.

"Yes! Come on in," Joe said.

Joyce came through the door with a flourish. "I have a little snack for you. I figured you might be hungry." She had a quart thermos of coffee in one hand and a dozen donuts in the other. She tossed her medium length, light blond hair, causing it to fall to one side.

"Is there anything else I can do for you while you wait?" she asked, handing the thermos and plate to Joe. "G2 will be here soon. So just sit back and relax." She left the office, and Joe enjoyed the hot coffee and donuts. Then he pushed the plate aside, and pulled on the new shoes. He bloused them to hide the fact that the pants were a bit too long. He sat for a while in the empty room, bored at not having anything to do. Just for want of something to occupy his time, he opened one of the desk drawers. He felt uncomfortable rifling through someone else's desk, but Joyce had told him to make himself at home. It had been his experience that just about every desk in the army held a little can of GI shoe polish. In the second drawer he opened he found what he wanted, and set about enhancing the shine of the boots. They really didn't need it, but he needed to do something to pass the time. He proceeded to buff and polish both pairs of boots. He went through this process several times, each time using a little water. He knew the polishing and buffing would make the boots a little softer, making them easier on his feet.

Joe was still working on the shoeshine when he heard the sound of heels clicking on the plywood floor in the hallway. He looked up as the door opened, surprised to see a young girl standing hesitantly in the doorway. She was slender, and dressed in navy blue slacks and a pale blue sleeveless blouse. She appeared small and fragile as she paused for a moment in the doorway. In the shadows her eyes looked quite large, black and luminous. They were fringed with long, black lashes.

Bristol followed close behind, holding the door open for her.

A look of dismay had appeared on her countenance, as she walked into the room. Bristol got to the business at hand. "Joe, this young lady goes by the name of Louise, she'll be translating for you. Louise, this is Sergeant Joe, the man I've been telling you about."

Louise gave her long, black ponytail a flip causing it to spring around, landing on her shoulder, and hang down the front of her blouse. She smoothed the shiny hair with her hand.

"Surely not. This small fellow is Sargento Joe? You make joke, no?" Her dark eyes flashed with irritation. Her petite four-foot eleven-inch frame making her appear even younger than she actually was.

Joe mentally swept away the girl's insults, protesting to Bristol. "You aren't serious! This is the interpreter you told me about? You don't intend to send this girl, this small child into combat?"

Bristol sat down in the massive brown leather office chair, and pushed it back as if lounging. However, the edge to his voice left no doubt as to his irritation. "Neither of you have anything to say about who'll go on this mission. Is that understood? She's your assistant, Joe. As for you, Louise, don't you be worrying about Joe not being able to do his job. He was the pick of more than a hundred good men. I make the rules here, so both of you had better get used to it." Bristol glared at them. "Now let me clue you in on a few facts. The government has quite a large investment in both of you. Joe, you're still in the reserves! Your carcass belongs to me. Is that clear?"

Bristol paused for about thirty seconds to let that sink in. "You've agreed to a duty assignment, and you'll carry it out, or I'll have you dishonorably discharged! You can kiss that construction job of yours goodbye. As a matter of fact, you won't be needing a job at all, if you get my drift."

Joe didn't argue. He knew that Bristol had the power to carry out his threats. He didn't like it, but he wasn't afraid of Bristol. However, he felt sorry for the small girl.

She trembled, and her hands shook. She had remained quiet since her first display of anger, but now she mustered up the courage to speak in broken, but understandable English, "Is not so good this man lead my people. We can't work with him. His light hair and light skin will give him away. It will be too dangerous."

Bristol looked from one to the other, then spat out a few choice expletives. "What's going on here? Hate at first sight? You two will have to learn to get along and that's, that." Bristol lowered his eyes to glare at Joe. "Are you trying to turn down this assignment? It's too late now, buster. There's more than your hide involved in this mission. You're already committed."

"Okay," Joe said, softening a little. "I gave my word, and as I told you before, once I give my word I'll keep it. I don't think it's wise sending a young woman into this type of situation, though. People will be getting killed, and her abilities to cope are undetermined. Besides, whoever heard of sending a female to fight a war? You're a man, and you well know, or certainly should know, the danger of sending a woman into a situation like we're facing."

Joe could tell by the look on the girl's face that this exchange between Bristol and himself had upset her. He knew that war is serious business, and she could be hurt or killed.

"But I am sending you to protect her," Bristol said, placing the burden on Joe's back. "Besides, let me tell you something, Joe." Bristol said in a gruff voice. "This youngster has seen more hardship in her short lifetime then you've ever dreamed about. Make no mistake; I don't have the option of caring about either of you. I'm treating you both like soldiers. I can't afford the privilege of caring about those serving under me. My only concern is the mission. Just cross me, and see what happens."

With a curious disregard for Bristol's presence, Louise looked toward Joe, maybe as a friend, for the first time. "Can he really cause that much trouble?"

"Yes, I think he probably could," Joe answered sadly. "Maybe we should start over. My name is Joe." Before he could say his last name, she bolted across the room, and put her hand over his mouth.

"We don't use names, not real ones," she said. "You will be Sargento

Joe, that's enough for now. Let me explain." Her voice softened as she continued. "We all have families and friends living in Cuba. If we were to be taken prisoner by Castro's people, they will torture us to try to make us tell everything we know. That's the reason for the name business. Louise isn't my real name. Maybe someday, I'll be able to tell you all the truth about me. I hope so. Maybe someday, you'll be able to do the same. But for now...it is enough."

She surprised him. Now he could tell she was much more experienced than he had thought.

Now she turned to Bristol, ignoring Joe temporarily, saying, "My people need supplies, food, clothing, and ammunition to train with. What arrangements have you...?"

"That will be Sergeant Joe's job from now on," Bristol said, cutting her off in mid sentence.

"Explain that," Louise said impatiently.

Bristol's mouth formed a thin taunt line. "Just as I told you, the Sergeant will be handling these matters from here on in."

Joe stepped between Bristol and Louise. He knew Bristol could get rough, and he decided to save the girl any unnecessary pain. "Looks like you're stuck with me, Louise. What do ya say, truce?"

Looking down at the floor, Louise nodded in agreement. "Okay, we'll talk. First though, tell me why you don't want me?" She tried to act as if it didn't matter, but the quiver of her chin, and her crestfallen face gave her away. Joe hoped she wouldn't be that transparent if caught by the enemy. He wondered if he could teach her to lie with a straight face.

Joe softened his answer. "I don't have anything against you personally. I would tell my kid sister the same thing. Do you have any idea what you are getting into? You must know it is foolish to take such a risk." He studied her momentarily. "You're so delicate and small."

That statement immediately fired her Latin temperament. She stepped closer to Joe, stretched her diminutive frame as tall as she could, and started a tongue lashing that sputtered back and forth from English to Spanish. Her hands were chopping at the air, like an auctioneer at a horse sale. Joe didn't understand much of what she said, but her meaning was loud and clear. He recognized fighting words when he heard them, and smiled.

Joe held up his hands in a pacifying gesture, trying to interrupt her tirade. "Okay! Okay! Cool it! Sit down, and take a deep breath. I've heard of these Cuban temper tantrums, but this is the first one I have ever seen. I admit I'm impressed." Joe now had a conciliatory tone in his voice, and surprisingly she obeyed, sitting on one of the chairs.

"She sure is cute when she's angry," Joe said, looking at Bristol.

Joe got his second surprise. Bristol smiled. Not a condescending one, but a genuine show of emotion. He looked amused. Louise had settled down, and was sitting demurely in a leather chair. Bristol stood up. "I'll leave you now, so you two can get to know each other a little better." He turned to Louise. "Play nice," he cautioned. Then he spoke to Joe. "I'll need to talk to you later, after the two of you are through scratching each other's eyes out. We'll need to go over a few more things before I leave Homestead. You'll need to get your booster shots. You should do that ASAP. Some of them don't take effect for thirty days."

Bristol continued, "Joe, there will be a jeep outside the building for you to drive, the secretary in the front office will give you the keys. You can use it as long as you're here." He left the room, closing the door behind him, leaving Joe and Louise alone together for the first time.

Joe lit a cigarette offering the pack to Louise. She took one and gave it back. He gave her a light with his army Zippo. "Do you think you can work with me?"

She took a small drag on the cigarette, but did not inhale deeply. She quickly blew the smoke out of her mouth. "I'm willing to try. It's not personal. I was really expecting some big, rough, and tough Americano ranger, but I guess you'll have to do. Maybe everything will work out." She sounded doubtful. "I certainly hope so."

"Well, I'm sorry you are disappointed that I'm not John Wayne. I sure hope I can generate a little more confidence from you. This doesn't do much for the male ego, you know." He could tell she didn't smoke by the way she puffed, and held the cigarette. He figured if she kept trying to smoke that thing she was going to be sick. "You don't need to smoke to prove anything to me."

Louise looked at him with watery eyes. Not able to hold it in any longer, she coughed, thrusting the cigarette into a small, olive green ration can, already bulging with sand and cigarette butts. "Sargento, do you really think you can do this job?" she asked, her eyes wide with concern.

Joe felt he was in way over his head, but could not admit that to her. She already had her misgivings. He hoped he could boost her confidence in him by telling a little lie. "Sure, I can do it. I don't like the idea of you going into this kind of thing, not one bit. Do you have any idea what could happen to you?"

Her lower lip quivered. A faraway look came into her eyes, as if remembering some dark memory of the past, that still had the power to cause her pain and sorrow.

Joe wanted to comfort her, but he knew that any move to touch her would not be proper.

"Sargento, I'm not a stranger to hardship or danger. I can do the job if you will let me. I'll show you what all I can do." She spoke with a bravado that was suspect in Joe's mind.

After they talked for about an hour, he asked, "How old are you?"

She hesitated, then stretched to her full height again. She placed her hand on his, "Seventeen, and almost eighteen." Her small hand was rough and calloused.

Work was no stranger to her. Her hand felt strong for such a young girl. Leaving her hand there for a moment, her ebony eyes looked up into the Sergeant's blue ones. He felt something he had never felt before. Something he couldn't quite explain. The touch of her hand gave him a warm feeling, and he was surprised at the intensity of his emotions. He wanted to protect this girl. Two hours ago he didn't even know she existed, yet now he knew he would give his life for her. Feeling such strong emotion, he pulled his hand away. He was working hard to keep his feelings under control. That could well be the key to the success or failure of the mission.

Although he was almost five years older than Louise, he had a suspicion she might be more prepared for battle than he was. He grudgingly admitted to himself that she would probably be a real asset, if not a pleasant distraction.

The logical part of his brain told him that the mission was too dangerous for her. Still he didn't have any choice in the matter. He would have to take her along or tell Bristol he had changed his mind, and was turning down the mission. He might have considered it before he met Louise. He still could refuse to go, but they would just send someone else in his place. Then who would protect her?

Knowing something about what was coming, he decided to go to the NCO Club, and have a beer or two. As he replayed in his mind all that had just transpired, he thought about inviting her to go with him. It would give him pleasure to have such a beautiful girl on his arm. He would be the envy of the patrons at the club. He knew she was underage, but if she didn't drink the hard stuff he figured it shouldn't ruffle any feathers.

He stepped over to the desk, sat down on the edge, and cleared his throat. "I think I might go to the club later this evening for a sandwich, and a beer or two. Would you like to join me? After all, we will be working closely together. It might help if we get to know each other better." He saw the question in her huge, luminous eyes. "Just a friendly night on the town."

She thought about it while she studied his face. Then with a slight nod of her head she consented. His heart skipped a beat as he looked down into her sparkling black eyes.

"Sargento, are you sure? I don't want to make trouble."

"There won't be any trouble," he promised. Knowing he had to get his booster shots that afternoon, he said, "Louise, we might as well get some use out of that jeep they assigned to me. I'll take you home now, and pick you up later this evening."

"No, Sargento Joe. I would rather walk."

"Oh, come on, go with me. I'll have to know where you are staying so I can pick you up this evening."

Immediately, her eyes lowered and her head drooped in embarrassment.

"I didn't want you to know I have been living in a tent," she replied sadly.

"I've spent a few nights in one myself." He grinned, trying to reassure her.

Looking up at him, she smiled. "All right sargento, come, I'll show you the way."

He followed her as she walked up the hall. "Wait a moment. I'll need to get the key for that jeep," Joe said.

She stood just outside the secretary's door, watching as he picked up the key for the jeep.

As they drove by other tents, the men came out to watch. She pointed to her tent, just a little off to one side. Louise smiled as she lifted her chin, in an attempt to hide the embarrassment that lurked deep in her being. Joe jumped out, ran around to her side, and assisted her from the front seat. She scampered down from the little beast, as Joe called it.

The men from the other tents were beginning to gather around them.

Louise greeted the men with a smile. She immediately introduced Joe.

The first man she presented to Joe was a fairly young man, obviously of Latin ancestry. "This is Gabby, my cousin, and my closest friend," she volunteered, momentarily linking her arm to his in an intimate embrace. "This guy over here is Sam," she added pointing to another young man with her free hand. "Sam is the one who takes care of most of our equipment." As she spoke, she beckoned for a private to come closer. "This fellow is named Carlos."

Joe shook hands with all the men. He thought that Carlos' attitude was a little hostile. The first two men were cordial enough, but Carlos shook hands with a nod and a grunt, then walked quickly back toward the mess tent.

Noting Joe's unspoken concerns, Louise said, "Don't mind Carlos, he's just a little jealous. He thinks I belong to him. I don't though," she said with a shy smile.

"I don't want to come between you and your guy," Joe joked.

"He's not my guy. He just doesn't want to accept my refusal."

She looked at the group and announced, "Sargento Joe is taking me to the NCO Club tonight."

Joe noticed the men seemed slightly taken aback by the news. He watched as they shook their heads in disbelief, talking to each other in very rapid and to Joe, incomprehensible Spanish. They looked at him, and shook their heads again.

"Louise, what is it? Did I say something wrong?"

"No, not really. They're just a little upset that I'm going with you this evening," she responded. "They'll get over it."

"Whatever you say," Joe said, relieved that she still wanted to go with him; despite the gloomy reception he had received from her friends and relative. He could still feel the hostile glances of some of the men as he got into the jeep. "I'll come for you around seven this evening."

As Joe drove away, his mind wandered to the task at hand. He wasn't looking forward to the conference with the government agent. He dreaded getting the shots even more. In front of the commissary,

Joe pulled into a parking space, and went inside for his meeting with Bristol. He was already there waiting.

"Let's go back where we can have a little privacy," Bristol said as they started walking toward some offices in the rear of the building.

"I see she didn't scratch your eyes out," he chuckled. "You didn't smack her one to keep her in line, did you?"

Joe had the distinct impression that Bristol would have handled the situation in exactly that manner. So he ignored the question.

"I don't dislike her. I just don't want to take her on a mission that she can't handle. In fact, I asked her to join me at the NCO Club tonight, so I could get to know her a little better."

"You did what!" Bristol grunted through clinched teeth. As he backed Joe against the wall, he asked, "What could you have been thinking? Do you have any idea what kind of trouble that will cause? The exiles aren't permitted in the club for security reasons." His face had turned the color of an overripe apple. "You've made both our jobs much harder than they needed to be." Bristol led the way into an empty office as he continued voicing his displeasure in Joe's decision. "The club has been placed off limits to Cubans. She should have told you that!"

Joe was aware of prejudice against black people, but this was new to him. He sat down when Bristol indicated that he should do so.

Bristol continued, "You have just made your first mistake, Mister. You'd never be able to get her in the front door." Bristol pondered the situation, drumming his fingers on the table. Finally after what seemed an eternity he lifted his head, looking Joe in the eye. "Maybe we can work this out to our advantage. We wouldn't want to disappoint the lady. Now that you have invited her, see if you can get her into the club. I think you'll have your work cut out for you. Get on the good side of the girl. Give her a little love talk. Say things she wants to hear. That way she'll follow you to the ends of the earth, and the mission will be a success. Watch your step tonight. If you do anything to make her back out, the rest of the exiles will follow her lead, then the mission will be in jeopardy. If anything happens, you will be held responsible. It will be out of my hands."

Joe, feeling a little cocky about the evening ahead, boasted, "I think I can take care of anything that might happen at the club." Again, he and Bristol were scowling at each other, and the thought ran through Joe's mind that, like he told this jerk once before, he was coming close to an old-fashioned butt kicking.

Bristol wisely changed the subject. "The next few hours are going to be very important. You need to make a good impression on these people. You can't let anything go wrong. For what it's worth, I believe you'll be able to handle whatever it is we tell you to do. Keep in mind that if anything does go wrong though, you'll destroy all that we have worked so hard to achieve. If you lose the respect of these people or if anything goes sour, they won't follow you. There is one more thing you haven't been told...."

"Just what would that be?" Joe snapped impatiently.

"We have received reports that Cuba is importing planes and missiles from Russia. One of our agents sent word last week they have four MIG fighter jets still in the crates, and they're pouring cement for the missile pads even as we speak, hoping to have them in operation soon. As you well know, the United States can't have that. Three of our agents have been killed, and another six were captured this morning. Someone obviously leaked their names to the Castro regime. I'm telling you more than I had originally intended this quickly, but things in Cuba have gotten totally out of control. The plan at the present time is for the Air Force to hit some of these targets from the air."

"I can tell you that one of your jobs will be to find, and destroy anything they might miss. Those missiles could target the United States. As soon as the battle is underway, take your people to destroy those targets. The Cuban military will be busy, and confused."

"Of course, we'll have maps of all the missile sites for you. It's too late now for me to get those maps to you, so we have a man who will come ashore bringing you the latest maps. This part of the operation you will be on your own. The exiles don't know anything about this part of your mission." Bristol opened a small gym bag, and dumped out a pile of colorful medals of various kinds, and several citations.

"What are these for?" Joe asked.

"You need all the help you can get, and having this array of citations on your uniform will certainly impress the peasants." Bristol pushed them across the desk.

"I don't feel right putting on something I haven't earned," Joe stated.

"Just put them on, and don't give me any static. By the time you get back, you'll have earned them. These trinkets should help you to get the respect of the exiles," Bristol said. "Besides, what do these dumb Cubans know about anything?"

Joe heard the sarcasm in Bristol's statement. He wondered if the United States Government was using him, Louise, and the rest of the so-called freedom fighters in some sort of scheme.

They continued to talk about the mission. What would be expected of everyone, the limit of Joe's authority, and about the forces they would be facing.

Joe picked up several of the medals and citations, shoving them into his pocket. "Where does Louise fit into all this? I know she is my interpreter, but what exactly does she want. How can I get it for her? My credibility may just hinge on helping these people get what they need to be successful."

"Tonight, while you're dining and dancing," Bristol said thoughtfully, "take a little time to ask her for a list. Take Louise and the list to the supply sergeant tomorrow. I'll make sure you have clearance. By the time you get done, Louise will think you're Prince Charming in the flesh. However, be careful. This young woman is highly respected among her people. If anything goes wrong, you'll have some tough explaining to do." Bristol started rummaging through his expensive briefcase, finally pulling out a plain, white, bulky envelope. He handed it to Joe. "Here's ten thousand American dollars and some Cuban pesos. Count it, then sign this voucher."

"What's this for?" Joe asked. He had never seen that much money at one time before.

"Make a good impression on that girl, then use the rest to pay off some of the locals to get information, or whatever else you might need. There should be enough money to show her a good time. A lot will depend on how you handle yourself tonight. See that you don't get in over your head. Anything left will be considered expense money. Use it however you see fit." Bristol walked to a locker, spun the dial on the combination lock, and placed the leather briefcase inside. After locking it up, he turned to Joe saying, "I don't think we'll be seeing each other again so good luck, and good hunting."

He watched Bristol leave the room. His head felt like it was spinning. All of this new information on the mission was a lot to digest in such a short time. Joe was glad to see the last of Richard Bristol. Arrogant was the word that kept coming to mind. Joe hoped that he would never see him again. He had met men like him before in the service, men who seemed to have a hidden, dark side to their personalities. It usually wasn't long before it was exposed. He had learned to keep his distance. No use grabbing a barking dog by the tail, then complaining when it bit you. Men like Bristol made his blood run cold.

Joe sat in that small room for a quarter of an hour going over his options, and trying to think of a way out of this mess without losing his job or going to jail. He wondered if his life might even be threatened if he declined this mission. He didn't think so, but he knew his standing in the military would be severely damaged. He figured he could get out of this mission, but though he had only known the girl for a few hours, somehow he felt responsible for her. If her life was on the line, he wanted to be there to do what he could to help her. He really didn't want the responsibility of taking her along on this kind of operation. Still, she would go with or without him. He couldn't help but smile. I've known the girl less than two or three hours, and she's already got me talking to myself, he thought. He wasn't sure what to think of Bristol. Would he keep his promises? He wanted to believe that an agent of the U.S. Government would be aboveboard, but he still didn't trust him.

Looking at his watch, Joe saw he had more than three hours before he had to pick up Louise. He decided to run the two miles from the commissary to the Base Exchange. When he was purchasing shaving cream, he noticed a little lapel pin with the American flag on it. He bought it for Louise, along with two Baby Ruth candy bars. She looked like a Babe Ruth kind of person to him. Joe wandered around the commissary for a while, checking out the wares. Looking under the glass counter at the more expensive items, he spotted a small black onyx ring. The stone reminded him of Louise's dark eyes. On an impulse he bought it, and tucked the small package away into a pocket of his billfold. Should he give it to her? Maybe, maybe not. After awhile he looked at his watch. It was 1800 hours already, six o'clock civilian time, and he was supposed to pick up Louise at 1900.

He shaved and quickly brushed his teeth in the men's room. It occurred to him that he had to go back to the commissary to pick up his jeep. It was a nice run, and soon he retrieved the vehicle and drove off.

CHAPTER FOUR

In a short time, Joe drove down the road where Louise stood outside the largest tent, waiting in the dust. She had let her hair down, and brushed it so that it glowed, reminding Joe of how a raven's wing might look with the sun glinting off of it.

Joe drove slowly into the gravel parking lot so as not to stir up a cloud of dust, and shut off the ignition. "You look great," he told her, as he climbed out of the jeep. Her dark blue skirt and light blue blouse were suitable attire for a jeep ride, and visit to the NCO Club. "Are you ready to go?"

"Wait one minute. I want you to meet some more of my friends," Louise said as she introduced them one at a time. They gathered around the jeep, seemingly eager to shake the sergeant's hand.

"So many names," Joe said. He felt slightly intimidated as they all jabbered in Spanish, wondering what they were saying. It amused Joe when every person introduced said, "Hello, amigo." Then they would speak in Spanish, and Louise would translate. It seemed to him that the interpretation was much shorter than the original statements. He wondered what she was leaving out. Was it good or bad? It went on like this for the better part of an hour. Everyone seemed polite and friendly. They showed Joe more respect than he felt he deserved. He could also tell these people held Louise in high regard.

"Sargento, can we go now?" Louise asked.

"Sure. It's getting late, and we have quite a lot to talk about." Joe took hold of her arm to help her into the jeep. He noticed she wore a strong perfume. Apparently, she had applied it kind of liberally.

"Nice perfume," he lied.

She smiled at him, her black eyes sparkling like jewels. "It is called Blue Waltz, my favorite. I only wear it on special occasions."

Joe went around the jeep, and slid behind the wheel. He was apprehensive about taking her into the club, especially after what the agent told him. He knew he had to carry on with their plans for the evening, and not botch it up. He started the engine. He noticed her long hair hung over the back of the seat, and he was concerned that it would touch the floor, getting sand and dirt in it. She waved to her friends as they drove away.

The jeep had a top, but no side curtains, letting her hair blow in the wind. Joe noticed it, and slowed the jeep. He said, "I'm getting your hair all tangled."

"Please don't slow down." She smiled at him. "I love the feel of the wind in my hair." The sound of the wind and the engine were so loud that she almost had to yell to be heard.

She seemed to enjoy the ride so much that Joe took the long way around the base. They drove for an hour before he stopped in the parking lot of the NCO Club, and locked the steering wheel. She sat in the jeep, fumbling in her purse and came up with a hairbrush. Brushing as fast as she could, she looked at Joe. "I should have listened to you. My hair is a mess."

Looking down at her he grinned, thinking how pretty she was, even with her hair windblown. "Here, let me help you." Joe said as he leaned over, taking the brush from her hand. "Turn around and face the other way so I can get at the back." He ran the brush through her hair, feeling the sensual softness of it against his fingertips. He forced himself to stop touching her silken tresses, and handed the brush back to Louise.

She started to get out of the vehicle, but Joe stopped her. "No, wait a second. Let me help you." He bounded around the vehicle, to open the door. He remembered what Bristol had said, and wanted to make a proper impression, but mostly it was for the benefit of the people going into the club. He wanted them to know that he considered her to be someone special.

Joe took her arm, and they walked toward the entrance of the club. Joe chuckled when he read the sign on the side of the building. The name of the club was 'Hernando's Hideaway'. After what Bristol had told him, Joe figured that anyone by that name would not be allowed inside the place.

Just inside the door, seated behind a small desk was a massive red-faced sergeant with a sleeve full of stripes, and a junkyard dog attitude. His job was to keep the undesirables from making it through the door. 'Sgt. Keller' was embossed on the name tag pinned over the pocket of his Class-A uniform. He stood up as Joe and Louise entered the room. Speaking in a loud voice, "You're not bringing that little Spick in here.

This club is off limits to trash like them."

Louise's olive countenance turned a bright shade of red, as she lowered her expressive eyes, the light going out of them.

"What's your problem?" Joe asked, stepping between Louise and the insolent sergeant. "I can go where I want, and she's with me. Right now I want to come into your shabby little club to drink a beer." He smiled while speaking in a low, controlled tone. Keller leaned forward to hear what Joe was saying. Joe judged the sergeant to be twice his size. He knew he only had one advantage, the element of surprise. When the red faced man leaned forward, his one hand resting on the desk in front of him, Joe grabbed a handful of hair, and at the same time pulled the supporting arm of the sergeant towards him, slamming the big man's face down onto the desk. Blood from his broken nose splashed three feet to both sides of the desk.

"Now can we come in?" Joe asked politely.

Keller tried to pull back, but the grip Joe had on his hair kept him from moving. "I see on your name tag your name is Keller. If you want to behave yourself, and stay out of my way, I'll turn you loose. If not, you can't begin to imagine what comes next."

"Go on in. Go on...just turn me loose," the doorman mumbled.

"Thanks," Joe said. "Oh, and by the way, I don't want to hear the word 'Spick' from you or anyone else in this place for the rest of the night. Do we understand each other?"

"Yeah. Yeah, I'll pass the word," he said, bleeding profusely.

"Good. See that you do." Joe planted his free hand in the big man's face, and shoved him back down onto the chair with enough force to tip him over backward. Keller fell to the floor with his legs spread, one on either side of the chair. Keller grabbed for his handkerchief, and held it to his nose.

With that same little smile that never quite reached his eyes, Joe nodded ever so slightly at the man on the floor, and placing Louise's arm on his, went into the club.

The stricken doorman began looking to see if some of the men at the bar might help him, but none would meet his eye. If the doorman had gone so far as to ask for help, their reply would have been, "Ies not my chob, man."

With the smile still on his face, Joe said, "Louise, I have something for you. I hope you like it." He pinned the 'Old Glory,' insignia on the collar of her blouse.

"Oh, thank you, Sargento. I love it."

"Please don't call me sergeant. I'm your escort for the evening. Just call me Joe tonight," he said.

"Thanks, Joe," she whispered. "You fixed that bad man good, no?"

Leaning over, he whispered in her ear, "We were just having a little fun."

They walked toward the back of the room, passing other men and their girls. Some had stopped dancing to watch the tussle, but when they saw the excitement was over, they returned to their dancing.

"Let's go somewhere else. I think I'm causing trouble here," Louise said.

"No. We're here, and here we'll stay. If anyone leaves, it won't be us." Joe took her by the arm, trying to hide the fact that he felt shaky and nervous. It often happened that way. During the altercation, he felt fine with the adrenaline pumping. After the fight was over, he would get to thinking about it, and it would make him angry. It was sort of a delayed reaction, and he didn't want to lose control. He closed his eyes breathing deeply to regain his composure.

"Relax, little one," he said. "We came here to enjoy ourselves, and have a good time, so that's what we are going to do." He gave her a hug, pleased by the eagerness in the way she returned it. He felt the anger drain out of him as she responded to his embrace.

He escorted Louise to a small table near the back of the room, careful to hold her chair for her to be seated. He intended to see that everyone treated her with respect. Joe knew that he was overdoing it a bit, but he was having fun. He would enjoy giving her a night to feel special. As they sat down, a tall, slender, carrot topped young man with a white apron hurried over to their table to take their order.

"Hi, folks," he said with a wide grin on his young face. "My name is Bob. I'll be your waiter." He lowered his voice, and leaned over to speak to Joe. "I watched you put that bully in his place. I should be calling the MPs instead of telling you that your first drinks are on me."

"Thanks, but that is really not necessary." Joe had lots of money on him.

"Oh, it's my pleasure. Most of the men in here would like to buy you a drink," Bob said. "Keller has beaten up on just about all of them at one time or another. He hurt one of my friends so bad he landed in the hospital. I got a real kick out of seeing Keller get his."

"I just did what I had to do," Joe said. "We came here for a quiet drink." Turning his attention to his partner, he asked. "Are you hungry, Louise? How about a steak and some fries?"

"I would like that," she said.

"Okay," Joe said, turning his attention back to their waiter. "We'll have two big, juicy steaks, two orders of fries, and a pitcher of draft beer with some frosted mugs."

The waiter quickly came back with the beer. Joe poured it into the frozen schooners, letting some of the amber liquid spill over the side of the ice-covered mug. Picking up his brew, he downed about a third of it with one gulp.

Joe wanted to discuss the upcoming mission with Louise, but knew that discussing it in public was out of the question. Small talk would have to suffice. He noticed that Louise sat looking at her beer, but she never picked it up. The ice had begun to melt, and moisture from the outside of the glass formed a puddle on the table.

"Would you rather have something else to drink?" Joe asked.

"If you don't mind," she said. "I've never had beer before, so I don't know what it might do to me."

At that precise moment, Bob came with the steaks and fries. "Would you please bring this pretty lady a coke?"

"I'd be delighted," Bob said, discreetly picking up the untouched beer before he hurried away. In a few moments he returned with a cold glass of Coca-Cola. He spoke a few pleasantries in his distinct southern drawl. It made Joe think of his own childhood in the south. He took a liking to Bob because of the polite, respectful way he treated Louise. He made a mental note to give Bob a big tip at the end of the evening. Besides, it wasn't his money he was spending, but Bristol's.

Louise and Joe stopped talking, and ate as if they had not seen food in days. Joe had grown up poor, so when food was placed before him, he ate it. As they were eating, he took a good look at Louise. In fact, he could hardly take his eyes off of her. Her deep ebony eyes looked like jewels, and her skin was smooth, soft, and clear. Her looks were everything a female could hope for, her tawny complexion was flawless.

Other girls he had gone out with would have given anything for such a beautiful golden sheen. Her lovely, almond-shaped eyes entranced him. Only a tiny scar marred her beauty. Tonight she wore just a touch of lipstick, not too much, just a light shade of red. If only she would go a little easier on that perfume, he thought. The more he looked at her, the more appealing she became. After they finished eating, he reached over, and took hold of her hand.

"Louise, don't let people like that jerk at the door cause you any pain. Never be ashamed of who you are. Maybe I'm talking out of turn since we are little more than strangers, but I am impressed by everything about you. You're beautiful just the way you are. Actually, I think you are the loveliest woman in the place. Please, don't misunderstand me. I'm not making a pass at you. We'll be working together, so that wouldn't be appropriate on my part. I just want you to know that I think you are a special woman."

She looked at Joe, and smiled. Somehow, he knew he had said the right thing. He started to realize that Louise was much more than the child he had originally believed her to be. Her dark, navy blue skirt and light blue blouse seemed to shine in the direct overhead lighting. Her wide leather belt and black cowboy boots had been polished until they positively glowed.

"You sure look lovely tonight," Joe said impulsively.

Her eyes sparkled with excitement as she smiled across the table at her escort, and Joe felt he must be the envy of every guy in the room.

"Thank you for bringing me here tonight. I never had so much fun before. I don't think I've ever had so much to eat at one time," she confessed.

That surprised Joe. Most of the girls he had met would hide their feelings, might even pretend to be bored, but this lady was totally open and honest about the way she felt. Maybe she had never had a young man take her anywhere, he thought. He didn't consider this a real date. He told himself that it was just a way for them to get to know each other. Even as the thought crossed his mind, he knew it was a lie. He certainly was treating her like a date. He knew he would always remember the way she looked tonight, especially the smell of that perfume. He was becoming more intoxicated by the woman sitting across from him. He thought of telling her how he felt, but didn't want to spoil the evening.

Instead, he wisely berated himself for becoming infatuated with her. If he were wise, he would not let this relationship become too personal.

Louise spoke in a low tone of voice, so no one else would hear. "Perhaps it would have been better to have gone into town or somewhere like that to talk."

Joe moved his chair closer to hers so they could talk quietly. "We can't take the chance of having anyone hear us. Probably the only safe place for us to discuss our mission is standing alone in the middle of an open field." He tried to make light of it, but she didn't seem amused.

Joe did not tell her about the little chat he had with Bristol. He didn't want her to know he had orders to show her a good time. Bristol wanted him to get on her good side, and to make her feel safe. Convince her that he was the man for the job. The break he had needed was the run in with the doorman. It had persuaded her that he was capable of taking care of her. They sat at their table with their heads close together, so they could talk over the sound of the music. Joe looked into her eyes as he said, "This is not turning out at all the way I thought it would."

"Is something wrong, Joe?"

He immediately noticed that she used his first name. That was a good sign. "No...everything is so right. I just never imagined that being with you would be so unsettling."

"Do you mean you don't like me," she asked, with a sad tone to her voice, "and that you don't want me on the mission?"

"Not at all. Just the opposite, in fact."

"Can you explain?" she asked, leaning forward until their foreheads actually touched. She didn't move away.

Joe froze for a second, the contact causing his mouth to go dry, and his mind to go blank. It took a second before he could explain. "Louise, you are absolutely the most stunning woman I have ever met."

She sat still, her forehead still touching his. Her liquid eyes started to glisten with the tiniest of tears as she said, "Oh, Sargento Joe, me too also. You are so much more than I first thought. I'm not sure how to say in your language. You make me feel safe and kind of warm all over. Is okay I feel this way?"

Her slight relapse into broken English caused Joe to smile. "Yes, Louise, it's just fine that you feel this way. We must remember though, that the mission comes first. We can't get into a position where we allow personal feelings to get in the way."

"I agree. The mission must come first. Many of my people are depending on us and we can't let them down."

As Louise continued to talk, Joe became more aware of her speech patterns. They indicated a strong education in the use of her adopted language. He had every reason to believe that she was from a family of good breeding. Earlier, as they were eating their food, he had been impressed by the way she held her utensils, and her table manners were flawless. Except for the overuse of that atrocious perfume, she was perfect in every way.

While they talked, Joe noticed that Louise's eyes kept darting back toward Sgt. Keller, and a group of sympathizers that had gathered around him. Joe turned around to look at the injured man. Someone had brought him a bar towel and a plastic bag of ice for the pain. Joe said. "I don't think that guy will give us any more problems."

Louise turned, and looked longingly toward the dance floor, watching the air force personnel as they danced with their wives and girlfriends.

He could tell she wanted to dance. Feeling kind of foolish, and hoping she would decline, he felt obligated to ask, "Louise, would you like to dance?" He really hoped she would say no, because the only other time he had danced it had been a disaster. He had almost broken poor Joan's toes…that had been their last date. She had always had a previous engagement after that. Louise couldn't have known about it, of course. "Yes, I would love to," she responded, "but I don't dance very well."

"Well, I've never done very well at it myself," he admitted, "but I'll give it a try if you want to, although I'm afraid your feet will be in grave danger."

"Okay, Sargento Joe," she said as she jumped to her feet grabbing him by the hand. "I'll teach you."

He felt foolish. After the tough man stunt, he figured he would look ridiculous on the dance floor. "The people here will laugh at us," he said trying to save face.

"I don't care, let them. These people don't know a dance step from a mule's backside. When they see us 'cutting the rug' as they say here in America, they'll turn green with envy."

"I ain't so sure about that," Joe said under his breath as they walked onto the dance floor.

Louise soon discovered that teaching Joe-boy to 'cut a rug' was just a little more than she could handle. He seemed to have two left feet and both of them were murdering the shine on her black boots. Laughing and falling all over each other and the fact that they couldn't dance worth beans didn't bother them at all. Finally, Joe begged for mercy, and Louise allowed him to escape from the dance floor, so he beat a hasty retreat back to their table.

"Are you okay?" Joe asked as they sat down at their table. "Did I break any of your toes?"

"I'm fine," she laughed. "That was fun."

Joe was engrossed watching Louise, and Louise was busy watching the dancers glide across the dance floor. Suddenly she turned, and Joe noticed the look of fright that crossed her face. She was staring at a giant of a man advancing toward them, coming up from behind him. He started to turn, but he was about one second too late. Two huge hands clamped down, one on each of Joe's shoulders. Joe struggled to get to his feet, but the man's strength kept Joe clamped down on his chair like he was sitting in glue.

Louise jumped up, knocking her chair over backward in an attempt to come to his aid. She reached into her purse, but before she or Joe had time to retaliate, a familiar voice spoke above Joe's head.

"I remember something about the way this little guy moves. I've seen him in action before."

Joe immediately stopped struggling. "You son of a gun," he said coming up off the chair when the man finally released him. "Don't worry, Louise. I know who this monster is and he's absolutely harmless." Joe was nearly dumbstruck when he found himself looking into the huge grinning face of the gentle giant, his old friend Stanley Kennedy.

"You see, Joe," Stanley said, "I never forgot what you taught me. Get close to the little guys, and get hold of them before they know you're there."

Joe's hand disappeared into Stanley's huge paw as they shook hands. "Louise, I want you to meet a close friend, Stanley Kennedy. Stan, this is Louise, the loveliest girl I've ever known. Now let's have something to drink."

As Louise sat back down at their table, Stanley spun a chair around, and sat on it like he was mounting a horse. "Hey Joe," he said, glancing around the room with a very wide grin. "Keller asked me to take care of a troublemaker. Have you seen one around?" He picked up the beer that Bob placed in front of him, drinking it down with one gulp.

Joe couldn't help but be in awe at how small the mug looked in that hairy paw. The empty mug made a clinking sound as he placed it back on the table. He filled the empty glass from the full pitcher Bob had placed on the table.

"I'm the troublemaker you're looking for, Stan. We got here, and that Keller jerk didn't want to let us in the club. He even called this lady a Spick, and you know how I feel about things like that. Remember the time we were on the street corner, and a corporal kicked that little shoeshine boy and called him a name? We both spent a whole month on the garbage truck for that one!"

"Do I remember? I can still smell that truck. It was in the middle of the summer. I think all they ever hauled was dead fish. Another thing, it happened to be the first time you got us into trouble. Before that it had been always me," Stanley reminded him.

Joe looked back, and could see that Keller was breathing fire. "I think Keller is getting a little upset about how you're handling this situation, Stan. Maybe it would be better if we leave. I don't want to cause you any trouble."

"Don't worry about him. I can take care of Keller. I got one more stripe than he does," Stanley announced proudly, as he turned one of his huge shoulders in Joe's direction.

"I heard you had died," Joe said.

Stanley laughed. "Do I look dead? That was just a cover story."

"How long are you going to be at this base, Stan?"

"I'll be leaving about the same time you do."

"What do you know about when I'll be leaving?" Joe asked.

"Nothing much," Stan said with a grin.

"I would love to talk over old times with you, and find out how you ended up here."

"That would be great. I'm gonna' be tied up in the morning. Can you meet me at the Base Exchange around noon?" Stan asked.

"That will work," Joe answered. "I'll see you tomorrow."

"Oh, by the way," Stanley said, as he got up from his chair. He leaned over to talk to Joe, so Louise could not hear him. "I know a little bit about the mission you're working on, and I've seen this girl with the Cubans. I'll be able to tell you a lot more tomorrow. For now, just let me say that we have a mutual friend, General Polk." Picking up a full mug of beer he drained it, and placed it on the table before he walked away.

After Stanley left, Joe and Louise stayed and talked until the club closed. They sat talking during the fast numbers, but tried a couple of slow dances to the tunes of 'I'm Sorry' by Brenda Lee and 'You'll Never be Mine' by Kitty Wells. The night out was the glue that cemented the relationship that had started under so much stress and doubt when they first met.

She seemed to believe that he just might work the miracles that their cause truly needed, and he felt confident she could handle most situations without going to pieces.

At 0230, the bartender went to the microphone, and made the announcement, "It's closing time, boys and girls. You don't have to go home, but you can't stay here."

Bob, the waiter, and a few other men came over to their table. Bob said to them, "Come with us, and we'll walk you to your car. Keller has a habit of waiting for people in the parking lot."

"Thank you, but no thank you," Joe said. "If Mr. Keller wants to entertain us we wouldn't want to disappoint him."

"Let them walk with us. It won't hurt," Louise said, so Joe smiled at her, and complied with her request.

When they walked out of the club, Bob and his buddies formed a protective shell around Louise, crowding Joe off to the side, which didn't make him happy at all. Evidently, she sure had made a good impression on them. Crowding in between Bob and another of her protectors, Joe managed to get close enough to help Louise into the jeep. Then he walked around to the driver's side. Each one of their escorts made a point of shaking her hand before they went on their way. Maybe they just wanted one more sniff of that perfume, Joe thought somewhat ungallantly.

CHAPTER FIVE

Driving slowly, Joe decided they could finally talk in private. What with the din of laughter and loud music, they had little meaningful conversation at the club. The jeep ride would prove to be a better opportunity to really get to know each other.

"I don't trust Keller," she said as they drove toward the compound where she and her compatriots were living. "I'm afraid he might know where I'm staying."

Joe looked across at her in the dim light. "You don't need to worry about him. If you think it's necessary, I'll curl up beside your tent and stay right here with you. From what I saw earlier, when I came to pick you up, I think anyone foolish enough to bother you will get exactly what he deserves. Your friends will make short work of a clown like Keller."

Louise looked worried and spoke in a hushed voice. "Really, Joe...I would much prefer having you on guard duty, if it's not too much to ask."

Joe tried to figure out what he should do. Maybe he had spoken too soon by offering to sleep outside her tent. The temptation to encourage her fears so that he could stay and keep her company was almost more than he could bear. Yet, he wondered truthfully if he would stay outside the tent. If he made a mistake and became intimate with Louise, he could blow the whole mission.

"Please, Joe."

Joe relented. "Maybe having me sleep outside your tent is not such a bad idea. I'll stay."

She moved closer to him, and took his hand and placed his arm across her shoulder, and then she held onto his hand with both of her small ones. Her body momentarily brushed against his side, as she softly whispered, "Sargento Joe, I'm leaving for Cuba sometime tomorrow."

"Why are you going sooner than the rest of us?" Joe asked, worried at the prospect of her being in Cuba without his protection.

"I'm going to make sure things are ready for you and the others. We'll all need food and ammunition for the battle. I need time to learn my way around the swamp," she said. "My father's family lives within a few kilometers of the landing zone where you will be coming in."

He pulled to a stop, shut off the ignition, set the brake, hopped out of the jeep, and trotted around to her side. She had learned to wait for her escort. He held her hand as he walked her to the temporary shelter.

"My lavatory is over there in that building," Louise pointed to a structure about one hundred yards behind her tent. One overhead light illuminated the area. "I have the key for that building, and I need to get dressed for bed. Will you walk over there and wait for me?" I'm the only woman here so they let me have it to myself. You can use it as soon as I get done, okay? The men use those over there," Louise said, pointing to some small portable toilets lighted by a single bulb hanging from a pole in front of each of the little outhouses.

"Thanks, I sure would like to freshen up," Joe said before she ducked inside the big tent. Joe opened his duffel bag, and took out a pair of blue jeans and a tee shirt. When Louise came back, he fell in beside her, and they walked the short distance to the building she had indicated. When they finished their toiletries, they walked back toward her temporary quarters.

"Do you happen to have an extra blanket? I'll roll up in it, then I won't need a ground cloth, just something to keep the dew off."

"I have two," she answered. "One will be all I need."

Taking the blanket she handed him, Joe retreated to just outside her tent. He spread the blanket on the sand, moving a pebble or two out of the way, he then lay on one half, and covered with the other half, rolling up like a cocoon. As he got comfortable in the sand, an old jazz tune ran through his mind, one that he had hated as a child. His mother and father loved it, and played it often. It was just an old scratched phonograph record, and the sound was tinny and high pitched. Still they played it over and over. It always sounded like a ghostly voice from the past coming across weak and muffled through the battered old hi-fi. The words of that old tune came to his mind to haunt him.

It's three o'clock in the morning - We've danced the whole night through - Daylight soon will be dawning - Just one more waltz with you - That melody so entrancing - Seems to be made for us two - I could go right on dancing - Forever dear with you.

It's funny how a tune will get stuck in your head, and bring back so many memories, he thought. Joe hadn't heard that song in years. Now each scratchy note was as real as it had ever been. He remembered the look his mother and father gave each other when they thought no one was paying attention to them. They seemed lost in another world as that tune played. He thought how accurately that old tune would fit the picture tonight.

Joe heard Louise ask from inside the tent, "You asleep, Sargento?"

"We should be quiet, and not wake the others," he said in a hushed voice.

She came out of the tent. "They won't wake up. They've been training hard all day. If we don't make any loud noise, it won't disturb them. Can we talk for a little while?"

"Sure. What do you want to talk about?"

"I have fun tonight, and don't want it to end."

Joe laughed. "You're the first one to ever admit that you liked my company. How could you enjoy having me step all over your feet?"

"You're not bad dancer for first time," she replied. Then she asked a real female question, "I think you have many girlfriends, maybe?"

"Not really," he said.

"No one do that for me before," she stated.

"Do what?" he asked.

"Fight because of me."

"I'm sure it won't be the last occasion in your lifetime."

Not wanting to spoil the evening for her, he thought it would be best not to speculate as to how much time they had left to spend in each other's company.

Let her think whatever she wanted, Joe thought. He had come to suspect that Bristol was using his presence only as a ploy to get the confidence of the exiles, for what purpose he hadn't quite figured out.

"I don't have time for boys," Louise rambled on. "I work all day, and when I come home there's always my school work. I never go out. Then my father, he is very strict, and he doesn't allow me to be around boys. He wants me to get as much education as I can, so I can get a good job, and help him earn money."

"Let's hope this will soon be over," Joe suggested, "and you will be able to live life as a young lady should. Do you remember much about your home country?"

"Mr. Bristol says I no can talk about that."

"He told you that you aren't allowed to tell me about Cuba?" Joe asked, getting just a little angry.

"If I tell you things, and you were to tell the wrong people, they could hurt my family and friends. They could make them pay for what we are going to do," she said. "If we get caught they will hurt us until we tell everything."

"I guess you have a point," he said, "but I sure would like to know just what we're getting into."

"We'll be in the swamps, and the weather will be hot and damp this time of the year. You'll need boots, and all the dry socks you can carry. It is almost impossible to keep your feet dry, and with all the snakes and crocodiles, it can be a little uncomfortable." Louise spoke so matter-of-factly that it took a couple of seconds for Joe to react.

"Snakes? What kind of snakes?" Joe asked, unable to stop an involuntary shudder. "I hate those things. No one said there would be... snakes!" Joe forgot to keep his voice down.

Louise thought it was funny and laughed. "Shush. Quiet. We don't want to wake the others. You'll just have to wait and see Sargento. There are some nice big ones in the swamp where we are going."

"You're not teasing about the snakes?" Joe asked. When it came to snakes, Joe didn't see anything funny about the situation. He hated and feared them more than anything else on the planet. He always said he was only afraid of four kinds of snakes: little ones, big ones, live ones, and dead ones. He was willing to fight the biggest man, but would go running scared from the smallest serpent. As a matter of fact, he would cross the street when he saw a pet store that had snakes in the window. He didn't even like to talk about snakes. "Forget the snakes and tell me something about yourself."

"What do you want to know?" she asked.

"Where did you grow up, for starters?" he asked.

"Before we left Cuba, I mostly remember how badly my father was treated. He just couldn't stand it any longer, so we left. A friend had told my father that I was going to be one of Castro's girls after my Festa. This friend helped father slip us out, and we came here."

"Castro could do that?" Joe asked, shocked.

"Castro could do whatever he wants," she answered.

"What's your life been like here in the States?"

"Not so bad as Cuba. My mama taught me English. You see, she was from the U.S. Father met her when he came here to attend school. They married, and went back to Cuba. When they first returned to his home, she started working for Batista. This angered some of Castro's guerrillas, so they took her into the mountains and killed her. Fidel eventually sent word to father that he was sorry, and he had killed the ones responsible for my mother's death. I don't believe he really did."

Louise told about the death of her mother the same way she had talked about the snakes, just another fact of life. Joe was glad she couldn't see his face in the dark. He stared out at the dark night, feeling sorry for the girl. The trauma this young girl had already suffered was more than most people suffered in a lifetime.

"I still don't speak English very good," she continued.

"Your English is better than my Spanish." Then he added, "But, of course, I don't speak any Spanish." He chuckled softly so she would know he was teasing.

Joe changed the subject, hoping to steer her away from the pain of her childhood. "Let me tell you a little about me. I come from a poor family, and we didn't have much when we were growing up. Understand that I'm not complaining. That's just the way it was."

"We didn't have much in Cuba either," she said sadly, "when I was very young."

Joe interrupted her. "Please, Louise, let's talk about what's ahead instead of what's behind you. I know now that Bristol was right. You will be capable of handling the mission. Someday, I want you to tell me everything about yourself, but for now maybe we should concentrate on the work ahead."

"Okay, Sargento Joe. I'll talk about some of the happy times I remember. How would that be?"

"Just great," Joe answered.

"It was right after we came to this country that I had my Festa Quinceanera."

"Fester what?" he asked.

"Festa Quinceanera," she laughed at Joe's attempt at the Spanish words. "It's a really big celebration for girls in Cuba. If we don't have a good dress for the celebration, then our mothers would borrow one from somebody. My father had saved mama's wedding dress, and had brought it with us to America. I was so proud to wear it. It was much too big, but I fixed it down to my size. You see," she explained, smiling with the happy memories, "when a girl turns 15 years old we have the Festa-Quinceanera. It's, how do you say, a Débutante Ball, a big party, a coming out party."

"Coming out of what?" he asked.

"Coming out of childhood and becoming a woman," she said excitedly. "We get to wear a beautiful dress and high heeled shoes, and have flowers in our hair. We have a cake, and all of our friends come and dance. Things like that." Her voice had started to positively bubble with excitement as she spoke of what had apparently been one of the few happy times she had experienced.

"And then you are a woman?"

"Yes," she said. "Then you are considered to be a grown-up and you can now hold down two jobs."

They both laughed. She did have a sense of humor.

"What about school?" Joe asked. "How did you get your education?"

"Mama taught me all she could, and that helped me when I came to this country. When I started school here, they said my mother had taught me well. I studied hard, and got good grades," Louise said proudly. "Now, tell me more about you."

"There isn't much to tell. When I was 15, my parents had a 'Getting Out' party for me. They told me to pack up and get out." They laughed.

"You make joke, no?" she asked.

"Yes," he said. "I make a joke."

They lay there in silence, apart but together, neither speaking for some time, just enjoying each other's company.

"Do you have friends in Cuba? Somewhere you can stay until we come?" Joe asked.

"We're not sure what we can expect," she said. "We hope so, but it may be only a tent in the swamp. Who can say? The people are very poor, but they are willing to share what they have. We will make do, whatever it takes."

Joe squirmed about trying to get comfortable in his little makeshift cocoon, leaving just his face showing, trying to escape the hungry insects that were dive bombing them and asked, "When you say we this and we that, who exactly is this we?"

"The others here at the camp, of course. Twenty of them will be going with me in the little boat. The others will come later in a troop ship. We are expecting lots of people to come out to join us."

Joe felt a twinge of jealousy at the thought of Louise being in the company of all those men, alone in the jungle. He mentally reminded himself that they were on a mission. They all had a job to do, and it came first. He would try not to think about what might happen between him and Louise until… well…afterwards.

They talked quietly throughout the night, neither wanting it to end. She shared one of her dreams when she said, "One day my country will be free like yours, and we can all have enough to eat. That has always been what I wished. What about you, Sargento, what is your dream?"

"I guess my dream is to be an officer in the military of my country. I love the United States, and that was one of the promises Bristol made me."

"Sargento Joe, what about a family, don't you want to get married and settle down?"

Joe didn't answer right away. He hadn't given it much thought, until now. When he didn't answer, she changed the subject. He figured she probably thought she was invading his privacy, but actually, he didn't want to tell her how he felt about her. They had just met, and it might scare her.

"Have you noticed the scar on my face?" she asked.

"Yes. I also noticed that it bothers you." He paused. "You're so pretty, no one will give it a second thought. On you it makes a very nice little beauty mark."

Louise giggled with pleasure at Joe's last remark. Then turned serious as she said, "My father came home drinking one night, and found me sitting on the floor doing my homework. I had to tell him that I lost my job at the market because they had learned my real age. They told me I wasn't old enough to work. He was also angry with me for spending some of my money on a skirt and blouse he didn't think was necessary. I bought them before I lost my job. He had been drinking a lot. He seldom got angry with me, but things had been difficult for him. He lost his temper, and went into a drunken rage. He kicked a lamp table. I jumped to catch the stand, to keep it from falling on my brother, and my father accidentally kicked me."

She grew silent and Joe detected sadness in her voice. Finally she continued, "I'm not angry with him. I know he loves me. The pressure of being poor in a strange land and having all the children to look after was just more than he could take. He sat down and cried when he saw what had happened. There was lots of blood, but it didn't hurt. Well... not too much anyway. It looked much worse than it was. He wanted me to go to the doctor, but I knew we didn't have the money."

There was a long silence, and Joe thought she might have gone to sleep. Then she said, "I miss mama." The night sky was just beginning to turn gray when she said, "Joe, would you walk me back to my building so I can take my morning shower?"

"Of course," he said, climbing out of the blanket to escort her across the compound.

He waited on the step outside, and in a very short time she came out. "Now its your turn." She waited on the step while he went inside to shave and shower. He put on his last clean uniform.

"Sargento, will you have breakfast with me in our mess hall? They'll be serving soon, and I would like for more of my people to meet you."

"I'd like that," he said. "I'd love to meet more of your people, especially the ones who will be working with us, and I hope they have some of that super Cuban coffee." After missing two nights' sleep I need lots of coffee, Joe thought.

As the sun climbed into the sky, dispelling the darkness, the camp was beginning to come alive. The men were leaving their tents, preparing for the day's work.

"I think it would be a good idea to let the men see that you stayed in the tent, and I stayed outside," Joe said. "I don't want to hurt your reputation. You stay inside, and I'll pretend to be asleep out here on the sand. We'll wait until somebody comes by and yells for us."

CHAPTER SIX

Gabby was the first to find Joe lying with the duffel bag under his head, and the blanket around his shoulders. He seemed to be upset when Louise came out of her tent, rubbing her eyes. She pretended to be surprised to see Gabby. He started speaking in Spanish, loud and excited. He raved on for a while, waving his arms the whole time. They conversed angrily, with Louise more than holding her own in the argument. It looked to Joe as if she was giving him a good chewing out.

She turned to Joe. "Sargento Joe, Gabby is angry because he thinks we slept together last night. I'm having a hard time convincing him that you stayed out here, and I stayed in the tent alone. I told him that I asked you to sleep in the tent, but you said that it would hurt my reputation."

Joe looked Gabby in the eye and shook his head. Pointing to Louise's tent and then to the spot in the sand where he had dug little holes for his hips, Joe folded his hands next to his head, shut his eyes, and said, "I slept out here." Then pointing to Louise, he grinned, and drew his finger across his own throat in a cutting motion.

Gabby looked at him for a long moment, and then he commenced to laugh. The young man shook Joe's hand, and pounded him on the back while nodding his head vigorously, "Si. Si." Seeing the angry look on Louise's face he looked toward Joe, rolled his eyes toward Louise, and continued in broken English, "Good, you do good."

Louise turned to look at Joe. "Sargento, you have made a friend of Gabby. He thinks of himself as my protector, and he won't forget that you didn't try to take advantage of me." She lowered her voice. "And....I would not have tried to cut your throat," she added with a slight smile.

Joe helped Louise into the jeep, and motioned for Gabby to climb in.

Gabby walked up close to the jeep, and held out his hand as if he wanted Joe to help him into the jeep. Joe grinned, ignored the hand, walked around to the driver's side, and started the engine. Gabby, laughing, jumped into the little machine with Louise glaring at him.

As soon as they stopped at the mess tent, Joe hurried to the other side to help Louise from the jeep. Gabby snickered, but Joe didn't care, although he couldn't help it if his face burned with embarrassment. Joe still wanted Louise to feel special. He took her by the arm. "Come with me little lady, and I'll buy breakfast."

When they entered the tent, a short, dark man ambled over to them. "Hi, Rico. This is our Sargento Joe," Louise said. "He'll be helping us with our work." Her voice rang with pride and excitement. "Sargento Joe, this is our cook, Rico."

The cook had the longest, black mustache Joe had ever seen, and a most engaging smile. "Mucho gusto... amigo. Sargento, you are the first one on this base to come eat with us. Most of the people here don't like our food very well. It's too spicy or too poor for their taste. We have different food than they serve in their mess hall. They have fresh eggs and they give us the powdered ones. We do the best we can. You are welcome to share what we have. There is plenty, and we are thankful for that."

The last part of his speech was in Spanish, and Louise interpreted for Joe. "He is not of this base. He is passing through like me. He's not like the others."

When they asked for coffee, Rico handed them two heavy, hand-warming cups, filled with steaming black liquid. After a cautious sip, they sat and ate in silence. Powdered eggs, black beans and rice was a first for Joe. He found the black beans to be tasty enough, but the eggs tasted like cardboard.

"Louise, I want you to make a list of the things your people need, and right here is a good place to start. You ask Rico what he needs most, and I'll see if I can get it for you. I don't know how much pull I have around here, but we'll soon find out." He hoped that Bristol had been square with him, and that he could get the supplies.

Louise left the table for a minute, and returned with a notebook. As she ate, she started jotting down the list. Joe glanced over her shoulder and said, "Be sure to add twenty dozen fresh eggs for the cook, and double the amount of training ammo you put on the list. I want these men to learn how to shoot before we go into battle. Now, is there anything else you would like? If so, put it down and I'll see what I can do."

As an afterthought, Louise added some fresh fruit to the list. She lifted her brow, and smiled before she bowed her head, and continued to write. She added two hundred cans of Spam. Joe looked at her curiously. "The men like Spam, and it's easy to carry. It will be a treat when we get into the swamps."

"I understand your army gets its noon meal from C-rations. I want you to ask all the men if they can get by on two meals a day while they are still here. Right from the start they'll want to save as many of the C-rations as they can for the mission, and maybe we could trade some of them for things we might need when we get where to we're going," Joe said.

She lifted her head and agreed. Their eyes met, and they both smiled. They were in one accord.

"If your list is finished, let's hurry so we can get it to the base supply," he told her, pulling his eyes away from her face.

"You mean I can come with you?" she asked excitedly.

"You bet your booties," he grinned.

She folded her arms and stomped her foot. "I won't bet my boots. I need my boots. Besides you should not talk to me in baby-talk."

"No," he laughed, slightly taken aback by the sudden flare-up of Latino temper. "I don't mean that you should bet your boots. It's just something we say, like over my dead body. It really doesn't mean what it says."

"Then why do you say it?" she asked, with a shrug and a flip of her head that made her hair dance across her shoulders.

"I'm not sure," he smiled. "I guess it's just one of those things that we say without thinking about it. You know, like it's raining cats and dogs."

"But it never rains anything but rain," she said.

"I don't know the answer to that one, but I'm going to surrender. This conversation has gotten completely out of hand. I need to bring you up to date on American slang someday. Now if you're going with me, you better get over here, and let me help you into the jeep."

When they arrived at the supply building, Joe gave the lists to the master sergeant in charge. Joe knew that if push came to shove he'd be able to get his own way, but he would rather not drop names.

The sergeant looked at the list for a long time, frowned, and said. "You've got to be kidding. I'm not turning all this stuff over to a bunch of...."

Before he could finish his sentence, Joe held up his finger and said, "Whoa there, sergeant. We don't use any word that other people find demeaning."

The sergeant gave him a look that was anything but friendly, but he chose his words more carefully. "I was about to say, Cuban Nationals. I heard what happened at Hernando's Hideaway last night. That just don't cut no ice around here, and you won't get no supplies until I get some kind of authorization."

Joe said, "All I can tell you is that G-2 told me to come here and to get the stuff on this list. If you have a problem with that, take it up with them."

"You ain't got no problem with me makin' a phone call, do you?"

"Not at all," Joe said.

A few minutes later the supply sergeant was back, and said, "Well, if G-2 wants it, I guess I ain't got a choice in the matter. The munitions will have to be signed out by the range officer. You want me to arrange for a truck?"

"That would be sweet of you," Joe said grinning all the while. He felt like saying, 'Get down and give me ten.' In a manner of speaking, that's just what he was doing.

"Everything on the list will be ready in about an hour," the supply sergeant said. "The food and other edibles are in that building." He pointed toward a large metal structure to his left. "I'll have the supplies loaded on the truck, but you'll have to show the driver where to deliver them."

The supply sergeant yelled at a private who was walking across the compound, called him over, and grunted out an order for the man to get a truck. "A big truck," he said.

"Will there be anything else?" the sergeant asked, not the least bit friendly.

"No, that will do for now," Joe said with veiled sarcasm. "You have been very kind and helpful. If there is anything else we require, we'll let you know."

"Yeah, you do that," the sergeant mumbled, turning his back so they couldn't hear the end of the sentence.

They watched as the supplies were loaded into a five-ton. When it pulled out for the Cuban compound, Joe drove the jeep ahead of it to make sure that the driver didn't get lost. He also wanted to make sure that Louise's companions knew whom to thank for the food and ammunition. That should put him in good with the men. When the supplies arrived at the area, they went back to the mess hall to get another cup of coffee.

The mess sergeant shook hands with Joe, and thanked Louise as they got up to leave. "Vaya con Dios, my friends," he said, and then hurried off to look at his fruits and vegetables, prime meats and fresh eggs; all were treasures in his eyes.

The sun was out and shining in the morning sky, by the time they drove back to her tent. Joe, looking around one last time, said, "It's time to start, Louise. Have the men who are to accompany you, strike their tents, and deliver them to the supply sergeant. Remind the men to make sure all their clothes are sterilized."

Louise looked at Joe with a puzzled look on her face.

"Have them make sure all tags and laundry markings are gone, and that they don't carry anything that says made in USA or by a USA company," Joe said. "Before you get to Cuba, make sure they get rid of any type of identification that they might be carrying; pictures, ID cards, driver's license, anything that may identify them."

As Joe helped Louise gather her few belongings, he was surprised to see how little she had. One small overnight bag held everything she owned. As they walked back towards the jeep, he looked down at her. She was such a beautiful girl. He knew in his heart that he was doing the wrong thing by taking her. He couldn't help but remember how she had looked up at him with those haunting black eyes, as they danced the night away at the club, and most of all how she had made him feel. With her in his arms, he felt ten feet tall. It was the first time someone had really looked up to him. He admitted to himself that he was flattered by it.

She had him wrapped around her little finger and she didn't even know it…or did she? If she did, he didn't have a chance. He knew that he would do anything to make her dreams come true, even though it might cost him his life. In another time and place they could go on dates, and get to know each other. Right now they were headed into a war zone, with both eyes open, yet still blind to the deception of their leaders.

CHAPTER SEVEN

The drive to the boat was too quick and neither said a word, each lost in their own thoughts. He picked up her bag and walked her to the ship. As she started up the gangplank of the shabby old craft, Joe said, "Louise wait, I have something for you."

She turned towards him, and he ran up the plank to her and pressed all of the pesos and most of the U.S. dollars into her hand. It was the money that Bristol had given him.

"Buy something nice for yourself, and pick up whatever you think is needed."

"You will be coming to help us, won't you?" she asked with a question in her eyes.

He wasn't sure how to answer, so he said, "That's the plan." It was out of his hands as to whether the mission went forward or not. He forced himself to meet her gaze. "I don't really know," he replied honestly. "It looks like the U.S. is committed, but it's not up to me. It's up to my government and your countrymen to decide what comes next. All I can do is wait. If they call me, I'll be there. That's as much as I can promise."

She held her head down as though trying to hide the scar on her chin. Placing his hand right on the mark, he lifted her head so he could look into her eyes. He placed a little kiss on that red mark that caused her so much shame. Next, he gently brushed her lips with just a touch of a kiss. It wouldn't be hard to make it a real one, but with a great deal of self-control, and the help of a wave that hit the old boat, causing the gangplank to sway, he pulled away.

"I'm proud to have met you," he said, "and I hope things turn out the way you want them to. I really don't know what is going to happen. Now hold your head up high, and be proud. I'll see you again if the mission is a 'go'."

Big tears were beginning to form in her eyes, and he had to turn away, quickly. He could see she was having second thoughts, and he had to admit he had some reservations of his own. Putting his arms around her, he gave her a little hug. She was so tiny that she felt like a small, defenseless child in his arms. She turned her face up to him, silently imploring him to kiss her.

It nearly broke his heart to deny her this one last request, but he turned away, afraid of the strong feelings they had for each other. Denied, she twisted free, and ran blindly up the gangplank. Looking back over her shoulder, she smiled, and tossed her head causing her hair to fall to one side, and he knew she understood. They must wait for whatever the future would bring.

Joe allowed the moment to be imprinted on his very soul. All the while he was thinking *if I never see you again, this minute will remain with me all my life.*

"*I will* see you soon, my Sargento," she yelled above the sound of the wind and surf. Louise moved to the rail, and Joe stepped to one side as a crewman lifted the gangplank. Immediately the tide began to swing the old tub away from the dock. Tears flowed down Louise's cheeks as she walked the deck, matching the speed of the boat and staying close to Joe for as long as possible. As the diesel engines engaged, they pushed the craft outward. Louise held onto the railing with one white-knuckled hand and waved to Joe with the other. "Sargento, don't forget me!"

Forget her? How could he ever forget her?

Out to sea and into danger, he knew her job had already begun. She was going ahead to help hide the supplies and weapons for the coming invasion. She needed to know where it was located when the time was right. Joe climbed onto the hood of the jeep, and sat there staring at the ship until it looked like a tiny speck on the horizon. He felt a gnawing in his gut. He drove slowly back along the winding road to the base.

CHAPTER EIGHT

When he approached the gate, the guard just gave a hand salute, motioning him on through.

He drove directly to the Base Exchange parking lot where he found Stanley sitting on the fender of a Ford Thunderbird convertible. Joe pulled the jeep alongside the bright red car, shut off the motor, and walked over to his old friend. Neither spoke for a moment. Stanley shook his head as he put his finger to his lips, indicating silence.

"Your car, Stanley?" Joe asked anyway.

Stanley nodded, and again motioned Joe to be quiet. Stanley indicated with hand motions that he wanted Joe to get behind the wheel and drive. When they pulled out of the parking lot, Stanley just pointed in the direction he wanted to go. They drove a mile and a half down the road before Stanley motioned for Joe to pull the car onto a side road. They parked at a wide spot, and Stanley reached under the dash to pull out a small microphone. Holding it so Joe could see, he then gently placed it back under the dash, and got out of the car, motioning for Joe to follow. The two men walked some distance away from the car before either spoke.

"I'd like to know what this is all about. How did you get an automobile with a built in listening device under the dash?" Joe asked. "What's going on Stan?"

"That's one of the little perks with this job," Stan answered. "I can drive it, but I can't talk to anyone about business while I'm in it. As you've seen, it's bugged." Then he added, "What's your part in all this, Joe?"

"They made me swear to keep my part secret, and you know if I give my word, I keep it."

"That's the reason I brought you out here away from the base," Stan said. "If I can't trust anybody else in the world, I know I can trust you. I gotta' tell you, Joe. I have orders to go aboard a ship called the 'Houston'. I don't know where the ship is now or the exact date I'm supposed to board it, but it will be some time around the first of next month. I'll be joining up with the 2506th Brigade."

Joe was surprised that Stan would talk about classified information. "This isn't like you to break a confidence, Stan. Why are you telling me this?"

"Because things just don't look right," Stan said. "Why didn't General Polk tell me you were here at Homestead? I think I'm in trouble, and I don't know what to do about it."

"Stanley, tell me exactly what you're doing here?"

"Radio," Stan answered. "At least that's the cover story we have been using. They taught me to build, and repair them. They're smuggling them into Cuba in pieces, and my job will be to put them back together. Like I said, that's only the cover. As soon as the exiles can take an airfield in Cuba, the supply planes will be able to land and take off. Right now, we're looking at a place called Cienfuegos. It's about sixty miles from Playa Giron where the 2506th Brigade will be coming ashore. Once that airfield has been secured, I'll land with the Brigade. Then I'll be heading inland to meet a band of guerrillas somewhere along the Covadong road. It runs through the southern edge of the swamps near the Caribbean. I'll have a map," Stan went on, "but you know I've always had trouble reading one of those things. I'm supposed to guide the B-26's in with a radio signal, and then the Cuban ground forces are to confirm the destruction of those targets. Another one of my jobs is to take over the operation if their sergeant gets captured, killed, or just doesn't do the job. Our people are trying to cover all the bases. The code name for this operation is 'Pluto'."

Joe stared at his old friend. "I've been briefed on operation Pluto. It's the code name for the overall mission. I know the targets are eight missile silos and four MIG fighter jets. Would this group you're supposed to contact happen to be called 'The Hillbilly Unit'?"

Stan looked surprised. "That's exactly what it's called."

"You should be happy to know that the leader of the Hillbilly unit is yours truly, Sergeant Joe Wells."

"Your unit!" Stanley said incredulously. "I can't believe it."

Joe continued to surprise his friend as he said, "Gargantua, meet Country Boy," and he held out his hand. Stanley stared at Joe's hand for a moment with shocked surprise

"You knew this stuff all along, didn't you?" Stanley asked with a slightly bitter tone to his voice.

Joe nodded. "Bristol told me about the missiles and the MIGs, and that someone would be contacting me. He said he hadn't planned to tell me that much back then, but he felt that if any of his people were compromised, I would need to know more details about the operation. He never told me that you were going to be Gargantua." Joe uttered a few choice expletives. "I think these people are up to something, and it's a lot more than they're telling us. What da ya say? Shall we stick around to find out what's going on?"

Stanley turned and looked up the road leading north toward the Air Force base, a wistful expression on his face. "I don't have a choice," he said. "Joe, I think you should try to pull out. You have a lot more going for you than I do, and I don't have any place else to go."

"You think I would leave my old friend to face this alone," Joe said. "Just what kind of a coward would I be, if I ran out on you now? Besides, there is a part of this story I haven't mentioned."

"What else could there be?" Stan asked.

"You remember that girl who was with me in the club?" Joe said. "Her name is Louise, and she's different from any girl I've ever met." With an effort, Joe pushed those last thoughts of her leaving on the boat from his mind. "Stanley, old pal, I'm in love. Don't ask me to explain, because I can't. All I know is that all the king's horses and all the king's men couldn't get me to pull out now."

Stan opened his mouth to speak, hesitated, and closed his mouth, shaking his head.

Joe could tell he had something to say. "Come on, buddy, speak up. If you have something to say, say it."

"Later," Stan said. "Later will be soon enough to discuss it. You don't know anything about this girl. Not even her real name; it's not Louise. I can't say anymore." The worried look on Stan's face made Joe very uneasy.

Joe decided he had better change the subject. "As I came back from the docks I noticed a nice cafeteria just a mile or two down the road. What do ya say we drive over there for lunch? We can talk about Bristol, hidden agendas, and listening devices. It might mean I would need to delay my departure for a day or two so you and I can coordinate a few more things. There's no doubt in my mind that neither of us knows all the facts about this operation. We're swimming in deep water here,

Stan, and if we don't cover our own butts, they could let us drown."

"How about it? I have a little of Bristol's money left. What do you say we spend it." He glanced at Stanley and knew by his grin that he thought it was a good idea. Before they got back in the Thunderbird, Joe said, "Stan, turn the radio up, and you drive this time. I want to see how many little roaches you might have in that thing."

Stanley went to the driver's side and Joe climbed into the seat beside him. Elvis was singing 'Don't Be Cruel'. Stanley sang loud and off key with the King. Joe looked the convertible over for more bugs, and continued his search until the T-bird pulled into a parking space at the diner.

Joe looked at Stan as they got out of the car and shook his head indicating he hadn't found anything of interest. As they walked towards the front door of the diner Joe said, "This afternoon I'll have to find the dispensary and get my inoculations and anything else I might need for the mission. If I'm lucky I might even find a doctor with some field experience, and be able to talk him out of the good stuff that every field soldier should carry with him."

The farther they got away from the Thunderbird the more comfortable they felt talking. They entered the diner, and looked around. Two men sat at the counter, but showed little interest in the new arrivals and went back to drinking their coffee. The other four couples in the place didn't even look up from their lunch as they continued their chitchat.

Joe led the way over to a table in a far corner, "It should be safe to talk here without being overheard."

When the waitress came for their order, they ordered T-bones with all the trimmings, and a pitcher of beer to wash it down. "I haven't eaten since four o'clock this morning," Joe remarked, "I was getting a little empty."

Joe watched as his big friend picked up his knife and fork, holding them like he was holding the handlebars of his motorcycle. Stanley had trouble maneuvering the knife and fork to his complete satisfaction so he picked up the meat in one huge hand, and gnawed off a mouthful. Joe watched with fascination as his buddy placed the bone on the table beside his plate, and wiped his hand on his shirtfront. Watching Stan eat had always been a memorable experience. He hadn't changed much. Joe knew from experience that the food the waitress brought on her first trip to the table would never satisfy his friend. Stan would need at least three more visits including the one necessary for double dessert, so Joe wisely ordered more steaks.

"Where are you staying?" Joe asked, while keeping his hands well away from Stan's plate. "Like I said, I might stay over a couple of nights. We need more time to talk about things."

"I'm afraid not, Joe," Stan said around a mouthful of food. He swallowed so he could talk. "I leave first thing in the morning to go somewhere south of here. I can't say exactly where. They have some Cuban people training at a secret base in the jungles. I wish I could tell you more, but that's all I know."

The thought crossed Joe's mind that maybe Stan could have told him more if he had wanted, but orders were orders. He would just have to wait and see.

"I'll be heading there to train until the mission takes place," Stan said. "I am free until 0500 in the morning. Once I get my stuff from the containment area, my job here is done," Stanley paused and looked at Joe. "There is one other thing I need to tell you. I've been staying in the same compound as your friend Louise and the rest of the Cubans. General Polk assigned me to watch out for her; of course she didn't know I was detailed to protect her. Jose Miro Cardona is her uncle, and good friends with a guy named Erneido Oliva. They are both very high up in Cuban politics. We have been careful not to let anything happen to his niece."

Joe leaned back in his chair, and pushed his plate away. Suddenly, he lost his appetite. Stan kept pulling one rabbit after another out of his hat. This supposedly dumb farm boy was a wealth of information. How involved was his friend? Joe just waited and listened.

"I've been watching you from a distance," Stan said. "At first I couldn't tell for sure if it was you, but the more I watched the way you moved, the more I was sure it was you."

"Then you weren't at the club by accident?"

"Not at all," Stan answered. "I followed Louise to the club, and by then I was sure it was you. I knew as long as you were with her that she would be safe. Then I heard what happened to Keller. The surprise attack, and I knew positively it was you." Stan laughed. "I ain't talked so much for a long time. I ain't found a friend that I could trust since we got separated during ranger school."

"What about that?" Joe asked. "I thought you washed out of ranger school when you couldn't finish the march that day."

"All I can say is, let's give General Polk a chance to explain."

"Can you contact Polk?" Joe asked. "I'd like to hear what he has to say about all this. I still believe we can trust him."

"I have his private number," Stan said. "I can give him a call."

"Private number for a general," Joe said. "Hey, Stanley, exactly who are you anyway?"

"Just a GI like you."

Joe shook his head in disbelief. If Stanley said he could call the General, then Joe had to believe him. "Ask Polk if he knows anything about these bugs."

Stanley took a little notebook from his pocket, laid it on the table, and started making a list of things to ask the General while he had him on the phone. "What else do you want to ask?" Stan said.

"I got a list as long as your arm. Why didn't he tell you about me, or me about you? How much does Bristol know that we haven't been told? How many men are involved in this operation? What's the CIA involvement? Ask him if he has the authority to fill me in on what he's gotten me involved in."

"Joe, I'll try my best. Want me to ask if you can come with me tomorrow?"

Joe agreed, and got up from the table, his head spinning from all of the new information. While Stan went to the restroom to unload the three pitchers of beer he had consumed, Joe paid the tab. After a short wait outside the diner, Stan joined him, and they headed for the car. While Stanley drove, Joe leaned his head back, and dozed during the short trip back to the base. When they drove up to the gate, Stanley produced from the glove box the paperwork for their entry. The guard glanced at the signatures, and stepped back motioning them onto the base. They pulled up in front of a small office building where Stan parked the car, jumped out, and ran up the steps, leaving Joe to wait in the car. Over his shoulder, Stan yelled, "I'll be right back. I'm gonna' make that call now."

Joe watched the huge man enter the building. Stan's shoulders hunched, and he held his head high as he walked. Joe could tell from

Stan's posture that he was upset. He wished he had warned him not to do, or say anything out of line to the general.

Twenty-five minutes later Stan came back out of the door with a big smile. He motioned for Joe to get out of the convertible so they could talk away from the listening device. "General Polk said he wasn't permitted to tell us anything about each other. He brought me here because he knew we would run into each other. He knew Louise wouldn't need protection while she was with her own people, it was just an excuse to bring us together."

"I wondered about that. What else did the old man say?"

"He told me you didn't work for him, so he couldn't order you to go. What's that all about? Who do you work for?" Stanley asked.

"I ain't real sure, but I don't think you want to know." Joe looked all around. There wasn't a person within two hundred yards or a building within earshot. "I could be working for the CIA, but I'm not sure."

Stanley, with a shake of the head, said, "I was afraid you were. General Polk said he hoped you'd go with me to look over our operation. You think you can pull that off?"

"I donno," Joe answered. "Can I be sure of getting back here for my flight on the 13th of April? I gave Louise and the others my word that I would be there."

"You mean Cuba?" Stan asked.

"Exactly. If I want to go with you, it'll mean I'll need to get in touch with Bristol. That jerk will have to give me clearance. By the way, where are you going? He'll probably ask me that," Joe chuckled.

"You think?" Stan asked, laughing.

Joe contacted Bristol and he gave his approval, which surprised Joe. Suddenly, Joe and Stan were a team again. Soon they boarded a plane headed for an isolated training camp somewhere in the South American jungles.

CHAPTER NINE

They arrived in Nicaragua after dark at a remote jungle airstrip. After a short wait by army standards, they boarded a helicopter for the trip inland, the last leg of the journey.

Joe was surprised when he discovered Stanley seemed to be in charge of the operation. When his friend barked orders, people jumped to do his bidding. After watching for a while, Joe couldn't keep quiet any longer. "How did you get in this position, and what's your rank? You certainly can't be enlisted."

Stanley just grinned, and said, "Like the T-bird, Joe, this is one of my perks. One that I've never earned, but I'm sure I'll be paying for it someday soon."

They were lounging under a large tree when the first shell hit about fifty yards in front of them. The light of the explosion produced ghostly shadows on the ground. Joe and Stan jumped for cover behind a nearby tree as the next shell exploded in the heavy foliage somewhere over their heads. As the second shell went off, Stan remarked, "The local drug people don't like us being here."

"You don't mean it?" Joe said sarcastically. "Should we find better cover? That last blast was closer then the first one."

"Nah, it's over," Stan said. "They hardly ever spend more than one or two shells at a time. I wanted to take some Cubans, and clean them out. It would be good training for our troops, but General Polk didn't want to take a chance on getting some of our people hurt."

"Then how about you and me finding the gun that's lobbing those shells and shut it down?" Joe asked.

"I've been wanting to do just that," Stanley remarked, "but I have orders not to do that unless someone gets hit."

Just at that moment a sniper's bullet buzzed close to Joe's head, knocking his wide brimmed ranger hat off. Picking the hat up, Joe placed his finger through the hole in the brim and wiggled it. "That did it, Stan! I'm in danger and I ain't got no orders to the contrary. Let me get my rifle. I'll find this little sniper," Joe said

"You know, Joe, if that was my hat I could go with you," Stan said.

"Really?" Joe stared at Stan's hat, and placed a clip in the M2 carbine. Stan took one look at the grin on Joe's face, snatched the hat off his head, and threw it to the ground.

Joe took aim, pulling the trigger twice. BANG... BANG...the hat skittered across the ground, two holes in the brim. "How about now, Stan? Do your want to join me in a turkey hunt?"

"You wouldn't have shot that thing while it was still on my head, would you?"

Stan grabbed his hat, slapped it back on his head, saying, "Let me get my BAR. You know, I kinda' like that little gun." He hurried off toward a tent in the clearing, stopping long enough to shout an order to his next in command. "Sergeant Jewels, you're in charge till we get back."

In the meantime, Joe watched from the darkness of the tree line, then began walking briskly in the direction from where the shots had come.

Now carrying his weapon, Stanley had to hurry along at a fast trot to catch up. He had ten clips of ammunition in the pouch around his neck, each clip holding twenty rounds of thirty-caliber ammo. The weight of the gun and its ammo meant little to Stan. Fifty pounds was a baby's breath to him. As he ran, he pulled a clip out of the pouch, placed it in the rifle, and slapped it home. Pulling the bolt back he slid a round in the chamber, and locked the safety. The strap across his shoulder let the automatic weapon hang at his waist.

Stanley and the Browning automatic rifle had become a deadly combination; just a touch of the trigger and death and destruction would belch from its muzzle. Catching up to Joe, Stan said, "I figure that sniper is the spotter for the bigger gun that's been dropping the shells in on us. This is the first time they've come that close to anyone."

They worked their way through the underbrush. The sun was shining brightly through the trees when Joe stopped behind the cover of a large tree that had fallen over. He knelt down, motioning for Stan to do the same. The minutes turned into an hour as the two men silently watched for movement up ahead. Waiting quietly was the secret. Sooner or later the sniper would move or make a noise, and they would spot him. The sun was just beginning to disappear over the horizon when Joe finally spotted a movement out of the corner of his eye.

Joe whispered to Stanley, barely moving his lips, and nodding in the direction of the movement. "There's our sniper. He's sneaking along through that brush just at the edge of those trees over there."

Stan looked toward the brush where the branches were still moving, just about thirty yards ahead and slightly off to their left.

"Do you think we can..."? Before Joe could finish, Stan's BAR began to spit fire and lead. "Hold it, Stan," Joe yelled. "Let's try to take him alive."

Under the barrage of bullets from Stan's BAR, the sniper lunged for cover. They had him pinned down. Swamp water behind him, Joe and Stanley in front, and the jungle to his right, he had only one way of escape. On the left was a path leading through the waist high foliage, veering off into a row of pine trees about fifty yards away. If their quarry did manage to get to those trees, he might make good his exit.

Joe and Stan were so busy with the sniper that they failed to notice the slight movement in the tall leaf grass behind them. A small group of men moved quietly like ghosts.

In a split second, the sniper broke from cover, running for the row of pines. A hail of bullets from Stanley's BAR fired into the ground in front of the sniper and Joe's carbine opened up behind him. That was enough for the sniper. He dropped his weapon and threw up his hands. They walked to the man and began to interrogate their captive, but he evidently didn't speak English.

An arrow whizzed by, striking a tree about three feet from Stanley's head. Stan pulled the arrow from the tree, not taking his eyes off the small group of men that had suddenly appeared. The men were naked from the waist up, their bronze skin blending in amongst the dark and light greens of the tall elephant grass.

Stanley held the arrow above his head in one hand. He broke the arrow like a twig and threw it to the ground, and stepped on it, grinding it under his boot. The group didn't appear to have guns, only bows and arrows.

Joe mentally berated himself for becoming so intent in the sniper that he had let down his guard. They shouldn't have been caught unawares because they were both well trained in jungle fighting. They understood how a mistake like this one could get them killed.

Surprised, but not scared, they didn't want to shoot unless they had to. "I wonder what this is all about?" Joe asked. "Do you know who these people are?"

Stanley just shook his head.

Joe turned to face the archer and yelled, "Any of you speak English?"

Immediately the crowd began to part and a woman walked through the men. As she stepped towards them, Joe noticed her dress was modest and appropriate for hiking in the woods. Her blouse was made of soft buckskin and her slacks were made from homespun material tucked into knee-high leather moccasins. A strip of rawhide about three inches wide was threaded through slits cut in the top of the footwear to hold the tops together, almost like shoelaces. The strip of rawhide served dual purposes: to lace the boot and to keep the critters out. She looked impressive. The setting sun gave her bright, red hair a fiery look. Joe judged her to be about six-foot four-inches tall. She walked past the men, stopping about three feet in front of Stanley.

"I speak English," she said, in a deep heavily accented voice. All the while she never took her eyes off of Stanley's face.

When her companions started to advance, Joe raised his rifle. The tall woman turned, lifted her hands, her palms toward her compatriots, and shook her head. They stopped and again squatted down, disappearing into the high grass, leaving not one sign that they were there, waiting. The woman almost matched Stanley's weight and height.

"My name is Tamara. The men with me would like to know why you're here? They're afraid you might intend to disturb their homes."

"We're training the men with us for a battle in another country far from here," Stanley said, never taking his eyes off of the woman.

She continued to speak to Stanley. "I was afraid you weren't coming back."

"You mean you know I was here before?" Stanley inquired.

"Yes, we've been watching for your return. We thought you were drug people, but you didn't grow the poppy flower or plant the hemp. We then thought you might be after those that did."

"We are not here because of the drug trade. I sure would like to go after them, but my commander said no," Stanley replied.

She accepted his answer. "Walk with me back to my camp," she said, gesturing toward a path that ran back into the hills farther inland. "It's not far, maybe two hours. Don't worry about your prisoner. He'll be well guarded. My men will bring him." She led them quietly up a path through the foliage.

Glancing at Stanley, the woman finally broke the silence. "I've wanted to talk with you, but I didn't think I should be so forward as to be the first to speak. Then I discovered that I had waited too long, and you had gone. I had my people watch your camp, and gave orders to let me know if you came back. Here in South America we have our own way of communicating. Our man at the airfield sent word that you were coming, so I came to intercept you at the clearing where the helicopter landed. The Cartel people got there ahead of me, so my Indian friends have been watching them to see what they were up to. For instance, did you ever wonder why they never sent more then two shells your way?"

"Yeah, that bothered me some," Stan answered.

"Well, the Cartel soldiers have about twenty people with arrows in their hides. My Indians have been shooting their spotters. So they have learned not to hang around."

"I'm glad you came out to see us. I wish I had more time," Stanley said. "My first obligation is to find those people and stop them from shelling my men." Finally, they approached a small clearing where the natives had built some small temporary shelters.

"This is my camp, I've been staying here, at a distance, so I could keep an eye on your group," Tamara said. "I would like for you to see our home. Would you accompany us tomorrow? Your men will be safe for awhile."

Stanley declined the invitation. "I'm committed to training these soldiers. I can't just walk away." His brow furrowed in thought until suddenly he snapped his fingers. "My friend Joe could go with you. What do you think, Joe? There isn't much I could teach you, but you might learn something from these people. Maybe I could get away a day or so before my ship leaves, and come get you. Then Tamara could show us that canyon on top of the mountain."

"Maybe," Joe said, "but first let's take care of our sniper. Let's see if we can scare him enough to keep his friends from coming after Tamara's group or us. I suspect he understands some English. Bring him here," Joe ordered and two Indians dragged him out of one of the huts and threw him roughly to the ground in front of Stanley. Stanley looked over and winked at Joe. Taking Tamara aside, Stanley whispered, "We need to scare this fellow, so try to go along with us."

Stanley turned and said with a loud voice for their captive to overhear, "Well, all right. I guess you can have him." Then he stopped. Looking down at the quivering man, he said to Joe, "Poor devil, I hate to leave him here with the cannibals, but you know they're hungry and have to eat. I wish he could talk to us."

"Yeah, it makes me sick thinking about it, but he can't be of any help to us. It's not worth the bother to take him away from the cannibals," Joe said.

Tamara, playing along, came to stand beside Stanley. She smiled down at the prisoner. Licking her lips, she started to pull out a large knife hanging from a scabbard tied to her waist. "He's just a little skinny and he smells as if he smokes, so that'll give the meat a slight tobacco taste, but it is free food." Suddenly, she shoved the knife back down into its holster as she turned toward one of the shelters, yelling, "Yoko, come, bring your skinning knife." Turning back to Stanley, she said, "He likes to skin them alive. That way the skin is not so tough. He just cuts a strip about one inch wide, rolls and dries it for bowstrings. It takes a long time, but he is a patient man. Besides, he enjoys it, so I let him have his fun."

Yoko hurried to Tamara's side, joining in the charade. Taking his knife out, he looked down at the sniper, and rolled his eyes. "Him make good bowstrings and I need new belt," pointing at the strip of rawhide tied around his waist. He started toward the captured man with the knife held high.

The sniper understood enough to start whimpering. "Por favor Señor no me sale aquí con los comedores de hombre. Tómeme con usted yo ayudaré puedo entender alguna ayuda de English mí por favor. Help you... You not leave me. I can help." He was shaking so badly that his voice had a tremor in it.

"Oh, it looks like he can understand a little English. What's your name?" Stanley demanded.

"Sidney," the quivering man whined.

Joe looked at Stanley. "Sidney! Whoever heard of a Spanish person by the name of Sidney." They both began to laugh. "Let them have him. He'll never talk enough to be of any help to us. He's not worth fighting these people for," Joe said, continuing the act. Joe wasn't keen on torturing the man, but he realized that if they scared Sidney enough, they wouldn't have to. The man just might be able to convince his friends that it wouldn't be wise to disturb this group again.

Looking down at Sidney, Joe said, "Maybe we could let him go.

What do you think?" Joe looked over at Stanley.

"Well, I'd kinda like to, but these people are our friends. They wouldn't take kindly to us letting their dinner leave." He looked at Tamara's back. He could see her shoulders shaking from silent laughter. Once she got her emotions under control she turned to look at Stanley. Her face was contorted and red from working so hard to suppress the laughter. "What do you say, Tamara? Can we release him if he promises there'll be no more shooting at us or your group?" Stanley waited for her answer.

"We've got Yoko's hopes up now. He did want that belt," she said, still struggling to keep a straight face.

"He has a belt and boots to match," Joe said, nodding his head toward the captive. "Do you think Yoko would take them instead?"

Almost crying now, the sniper said, "Take them. Take them."

"Boot not fit. Him keep 'em. Please me need bowstring. Can start at ankle, strip it up over his shoulder, then down his backside," Yoko said, looking disappointed.

Joe stared down at the captive while speaking to Tamara. "Will you release him if he promises to have his people leave the valley?"

"If we catch him or anyone of them again, we won't be so kind," Tamara threatened. "Cut him loose."

Grumbling, Yoko cut the straps holding his hands and feet. Then turning, he stalked away still playing the part of a disappointed villain.

Stanley bent over and with one hand grabbed Sidney by the back of his trousers and roughly lifted him off of the ground, standing him on his feet. Then with the side of his foot he pushed the man onto his backside, sending him sprawling back down the trail the way they had come. After regaining his footing, Sidney started to run. He never looked back. He just kept running until he was out of sight.

Tamara turned to Stanley, saying, "I don't think we'll have any more trouble with that bunch. That guy won't quit running until he gets back to his camp."

"As long as they don't brother your people after we're gone," Stanley said.

"I wouldn't worry about that. We don't come down here often. I heard you were back, so I came to see you. I thought we might be compatible with you being even bigger than myself."

Stanley stared down at the ground for a moment and then he lifted sad eyes. "I'm afraid I'll have to leave now so I can get back to my troops. I've been away too long." He turned to speak to Joe. "You go with them. Find out if they can teach you how to be so quiet in the jungle. Learn how to sneak up on a man without being seen, like these natives do."

"I'll go up the mountain with Joe, but just to get him settled. I'll be back in camp tomorrow. I won't look for you again," she told Stanley. "You'll have to come to me, now. You're your own man. I won't interfere with that. When you decide to come back, I'll be waiting." She stopped him before he turned to go. "What shall I call you? I don't even know your name."

"Gargantua," Joe broke in, with a mischievous grin.

Stanley nodded his head. "That'll do for now." He grabbed his BAR and trotted off through the jungle, backtracking down the trail to where his troops were camped.

CHAPTER TEN

Joe noticed his aching leg muscles. They had been walking uphill since midnight. Daybreak found them still climbing toward the mountain.

As they walked, Tamara reached into the pouch she carried and handed Joe a large chunk of jerky. "Mountain Goat," she informed him. She pointed to a spot near the top of the hill. "We should get there around noon. They'll have lunch ready for us when we arrive."

Joe glanced at his watch. It was just 1100 hours when they came to the foot of a high cliff stretching for many miles. They continued to walk along the foot of the cliff for another half-hour. At last, Tamara nodding towards a small patch of underbrush, said, "Over there." Pausing for a moment, Joe turned to glance back in the direction they had come. He let his eyes scan the mountain, taking a moment to admire the beauty all around them. The tall treetops protruded through the fog that hovered over the jungle floor below. He turned back just in time to see Tamara disappear into the small patch of vegetation. The natives had vanished.

Joe quickly followed after Tamara, finding himself in a small cave like fissure in the rock wall that jutted out from the face of the cliff. It was well hidden by the vines and foliage. Joe looked about, the close space making him feel a bit claustrophobic. He caught up to Tamara and the natives as they moved very slowly, brushing away any tracks left among the rocks. The two-mile trek through the overhanging crevasse took just over a half-hour. Looking out from the edge of the fissure, Joe could see a large valley, its natural beauty stretching out as far as the eye could see.

Tamara retraced her footsteps back to Joe. She looked out across the beautiful valley. "We have all we need right here. This valley belonged to my father and mother. It was a gift from the chief of this tribe. They are descendants of the Aztec Indians." Tamara pointed out a large log building. "My private quarters. You're welcome to stay there until it is time for you to leave."

When they entered the camp, Joe saw an open pit with a roaring fire burning inside. Two women stood at each end turning a crank on a spit that held two browned mountain goats. They had been skinned and stuffed with vegetables, then stitched together with a wire thread. The smell of roasting meat permeated the air. Joe's stomach growled, reminding him that he hadn't eaten anything but that piece of jerky.

He looked around noticing lots of smaller log cabins nestled back under the lip of the cliff, hidden from the air, all looking sturdy and well built.

"We've been watching your people train. We think we can help you, if you'll stay and learn from us," Tamara said. While she talked she took plates from the table made from logs expertly placed together and planed down to make them smooth. The legs consisted of two large stumps fastened underneath. The women piled food on the table. Passing one of the plates to Joe, she said, "We all come together for meals whenever possible. I sent word on ahead when I knew you had agreed to come with me. We celebrate."

Joe thought about what she had said. "I didn't hear you tell any one to come ahead and if you did, how could they have gotten here that much ahead of us?"

A huge smile settled on the woman's plain face. "I sent Yoko up a high tree and he signaled them using a hand mirror." A mischievous gleam danced in her eyes. "You thought it would be something mysterious."

Joe grinned. "Nice to see you have a sense of humor. I think Yoko shimmying up a tree to send smoke signals with a piece of glass is mysterious enough."

"Yoko is a good man. His mother came with us from the islands. His father was a Japanese soldier killed in the war." As she spoke, Tamara took the knife from a sheath on her belt. She cut two huge pieces of the meat for her and Joe. She placed them on the plates. By that time a large group of people had gathered for the noon meal. "We come together once a week like this for a community meal. It keeps us in touch with each other, and we usually settle any disputes, but in honor of our guest we will not do that today."

"It impresses me how these people move without being seen. That skill would be a great asset in a gorilla operation." Joe took a bite of the succulent meat. "This is good." Joe continued to talk as he ate the hearty meal. "I would like to learn how to move through the jungle without being detected. In addition, I noticed the men make their own weapons. Do you think they would teach me how to survive here?"

Tamara licked the grease from her fingers. "I don't know how much they can teach you in just three weeks, but I'll ask them."

The ranger training had been the finest available, but Joe knew he needed an edge if he was to survive in the wilderness. These people knew the brush and how to use it to their advantage. Joe soon found that the Aztecs excelled at stealth, passing down through generations, the art of seeing but not being seen. They had learned to stand perfectly still for hours. Their perseverance paid off when an enemy came into their territory. The men agreed to train Joe and actually seemed to enjoy the diversion.

Joe quickly found it wasn't easy, but he learned to breathe with short shallow breaths. He learned to evade an enemy by submerging himself in water and breathing through a hollow reed. He had learned to move quietly in the woods with the rangers, but the natives were advanced in their method of training. It took lots of patience. He learned if he stood perfectly still, it was hard for anyone to spot a target that didn't move, even in very sparse cover. The three and a half weeks were over much too soon. Now it was time for him to leave.

As he walked toward the airstrip hoping to catch Stanley, he met Tamara coming the other way. She stopped for a moment to say, "He's gone. He left this morning. He said you were his best friend?"

"We try to look out for each other," Joe said.

"He said you could be trusted to not say anything about us or our place here on the mountain," she said.

Joe answered with a nod of his head. "Is Stanley coming back or did he say?"

"He said as soon as he could fulfill his duty to his country, he would be back." Looking a little sad, she asked, "Do you think he will ever come back?"

Joe liked the big woman. "Stanley's a man of his word. If he said he'll be back, he *will* be back." He saw the look of hope that passed over her face.

"This is such a beautiful place. I hope we can all come back someday."

"You'll be welcome," she said.

"I'd better get on down the mountain. I've a plane to catch," Joe said, as he turned and trotted off down the trail, turning once to wave goodbye. Hurrying on down the mountainside, Joe was surprised at how fit he felt. The three and a half weeks he had spent with the natives had left Joe in better physical condition than when he had arrived. The diet had been mostly vegetarian and natural herbs. He breathed in the clean mountain air. He ran without feeling winded. Fortunately, his cigarettes had run out the second day up on the mountain and his lungs felt clear.

CHAPTER ELEVEN

When he got back to the camp, he found out that the helicopter had just returned from taking the last of Stanley's group to the Houston, the ship that was to deposit them on the Cuban beach five days later. Running and stooping to avoid the whirling chopper blades, Joe climbed in beside the pilot. When the helicopter whirled up into the air, Joe looked back trying to pick out the spot on the mountainside where he had spent the last three weeks. The compound was well hidden, and Joe couldn't see anything but trees. Wondering if he would ever see this place again, he felt a bit nostalgic. He pushed the thoughts from his mind.

Leaning back, he slept until the whirlybird landed a half-hour later. He roused himself just long enough to board the plane for the Homestead Air Base. Then he went back to sleep. His past experience had taught him to ignore the crew and to go about his own business. The only thing he wanted now was some shuteye.

Joe came awake with the pilot shaking his shoulder. "Wake up, Sergeant. You don't want to sleep your life away," he laughed at his own tired old joke.

Humoring the pilot, even though he felt grouchy, he smiled. He got up and gathered his things.

A military staff car was parked next to the runway with a staff sergeant standing next to the left front fender. "You must be Sergeant Wells," the young man said.

"That's me."

"Let me help you put your things in the car." He lifted Joe's bag and deposited it on the back seat. "I'm your chauffeur. I have orders to hustle your buns off to building eighty-two as soon as I can. Major Payne, General Polk's aide, will be waiting for you. You have a four-hour layover while they fuel and load the old gooney bird. By the way, my name is Bill. Can I get you something from the base kitchen? The officer's mess is still open."

"No, thanks. Just take me to my gear. I want to make sure I have everything I need for my mission," Joe said.

"The stuff you left for safekeeping has been moved, locker and all, to building eighty-two. You'll be able to pick it all up there," Bill told him, while swinging the vehicle around to drop Joe off.

Joe's meeting with the Major was a disappointment. He didn't give him any new information. "Look out for your people and don't take anything with you that could tie you to the USA. Remember to strip your clothing of anything leading back to the states. Cut out all labels. Good luck, soldier. I'll see you when you return. You will report directly to me. Is that understood?"

"Yes, sir."

"You'll find your things in the office next door. I think you'll find a nice surprise for you there. Dismissed!" the major shouted.

Joe left the major's office almost at a run, hurrying to get all his gear before the plane left him behind. When he opened the door of his locker, a Green Beret fell to the floor. He picked it up. Tucked into the beret was an envelope marked, Personal for Sergeant Joe Wells only. Ripping the envelope open, he found two handwritten notes. He read the first one. "PLACE ME ON YOUR HEAD AND WEAR ME WITH PRIDE, SIR. YOU'LL HAVE EARNED ME." I know just how much you wanted this! Now it's yours. Good luck and good hunting. It was signed, General Alexander H. Polk.

He quickly read the other short note. See you soon, Joe. Take care of yourself. Remember to cover your backside. Your friend, Stanley Kennedy

Joe removed the wide-brimmed ranger hat, placed it inside his shirt, and slapped the beret on his head. He proudly walked toward the waiting plane. He was loaded down with his rucksack, rifle, and a heavy pack filled with ammunition. He tried to strike up a conversation with the pilot, but this fellow couldn't speak English, or perhaps, just wasn't in the mood to talk. He started the single engine and they took off.

The old high-winged craft seemed to struggle to get airborne, bucked, and shuddered at the slightest head wind. They flew so close to the ground that Joe wasn't sure if they had really taken off.

After what seemed a long time, they landed at a remote airstrip where he once again, changed planes. This one was much larger. It was a C-47 transport that had been stripped down to the bare walls. There was a bench made from a wooden plank, but not much else. All of the numbers and insignias on the wings and tail had been painted over with olive drab paint, so there was nothing to connect it to the U.S. It was getting dark when the plane left the ground and flew due south for the ninety-mile crossing. The mission was a 'go', like it or not, and Joe was going to be a part of that mission.

Louise had told him of her dream of freeing her country from a tyrant. Joe had a dream of becoming an officer in the army. He was looking forward to seeing Louise again. His thoughts came to an abrupt end when an annoying buzzer sounded and a red light came on as they approached the drop zone. Certainly, they couldn't have made it all the way to Cuba so quickly. They were welcomed by small arms fire. Fear made Joe feel sick to his stomach. He realized the people on the ground were trying to kill him. This was a new experience. Sure he had made a few folks angry, but only one of them had come after him with a gun. Soon, he would be going out that door into an uncertain future, or perhaps, certain death. Small caliber rounds made a plinking sound as they hit the belly and wings of the old transport. Anti-aircraft shells exploded all around them rocking the plane, and the night sky was shattered by their thunder.

Joe sat staring at the exit sign just above the door, shivering with nerves and from the cold. The old C-47 had taken several hits and was flying on only one engine. He had trained to parachute but had never actually jumped. He still hadn't completely conquered his fear of heights. He figured their altitude was a tad over 11,000 feet. He wondered why they were flying so high. He didn't like it. The higher the plane, the longer he would be exposed to ground fire.

One member of the crew finished placing the cargo boxes next to the door, looked at Joe and said in English, "Sorry, I no have time to introduce myself before. My name is Lopez." He picked up a parachute, shoved it into Joe's hands, and said with a gap-toothed grin, "Here's your parachute, sergeant. Put it on." Lopez spoke with a slight accent. He looked and smelled like he had not seen a bathtub, razor, or a bar of soap in weeks and his breath had the odor of a cesspool. As he turned, Joe could see that the back and underarms of his shirt were wet where he had been perspiring heavily, in spite of the fact that the temperature inside the plane had dropped to almost freezing.

Joe inspected the canvas bag containing the parachute. His heart sank and he wondered about its safety. The straps were tattered and worn. On further inspection he discovered the metal buckles were so old they were even bent out of shape.

"Did you pack this thing, Lopez?"

"No, sergeant. I didn't, but I watched them pack it." Lopez smiled knowingly. "Don't worry, it will hold you. Now let's be getting into it. You have only twenty minutes before the jump. Which one of these extras do you want, the ammunition pack or the emergency back-up chute?"

Joe knew he was taking a chance if he didn't choose a back-up chute, but he figured it would probably be in bad shape too, so he decided to take the pack with the ammunition. He reasoned that if he made it safely to the ground, he would need the extra bullets. "I'll take the ammo."

A rope about ten feet long was suspended from Joe's rucksack holding his gear. It would arrive on the ground a split second ahead of him, to reduce the impact of the landing. His carbine was strapped to his body by its rifle sling along with about thirty pounds of ammo in the front pack. Joe felt the full weight of the combat load when he stood up. The equipment, along with the rest of his gear, weighed nearly eighty pounds.

"Check to make sure all these straps and buckles are fastened tightly." Joe felt trapped under all the weight.

Lopez smiled and tugged on the straps. "Is okay." Then he took hold of the strap fastened to his own safety harness hooking it onto a cable that stretched over the exit door of the plane. He then reached over, grabbed the handle of the door, and quickly slid it open. The wind and engine noise came rushing into the plane along with the smell of burnt gunpowder and smoke. Lopez attached the ripcords of the cargo chutes to the cable and began to push the cases of supplies out the door.

Joe moved slowly toward the opening, his legs starting to go numb from the tight straps of his chute. Stamping his feet, he tried to get some circulation back into his lower limbs. Reaching up, he snapped the hook of his static strap onto the cable before giving it three hard yanks to make sure it was secure. Now he moved to the door and found himself staring out into the emptiness of the night sky. Everything was pitch black except for what appeared to be fireflies darting all about the plane. He wondered what those little lights were. Joe knew they were much too high for lightning bugs. His question was soon answered when one firefly came through the fuselage of the old plane and with it the realization that these were tracer bullets from small arms fire.

Anti-aircraft shells were bursting all around the crippled plane as it made its last pass over the drop zone.

Joe stood poised in the open door of the old plane, fear sliding her cold fingers around his throat. Although it was cold at this altitude, his hands were sweating as he gripped the edges of the door so tightly that his knuckles turned white. No way I'm jumping out of this plane. I'd have to be crazy, he thought, looking out into the black hole. I'm staying put until this plane lands and nobody is going to tell me any different.

Suddenly, he felt a big foot in the middle of his back. Before he could protest, he felt a shove that thrust him from the plane, sending him out into space just like the cork from a bottle of cheap champagne. Terrified, he clutched at the air while falling helplessly through the dark void. An instant later he felt a tug as the strap tightened enough to pull him into an upright position. That tug should have opened his parachute, but it only pulled the pilot chute part of the way out of its pack. Most people yell Geronimo as they jump, but Joe missed that opportunity. When the static line failed to do its job, he remembered his training, and reached over his shoulder to pull the parachute out by hand. He had already traveled a half-mile, gaining speed with every second in free fall. Joe figured he was traveling about one hundred and twenty five miles per hour by now. He could hardly breathe. He hoped he wouldn't pass out. The noise of the wind and the flapping chute only added to his terror. His thoughts ran rampant. Was Louise down there? Would she be the one to find his body?

He closed his eyes to avoid seeing the ground rushing up to meet him. He heard a loud pop when the canopy deployed and he began to slow down. He sighed in relief. As he floated toward the ground, he noticed his trousers were wet on the inside of his legs. Oh, great! he thought. It's bad enough that someone threw me out of the plane, now I have to wet myself. Joe landed so hard that he had the breath knocked out of him. Disoriented, he heard someone call out. He lay near the road in about eighteen inches of water and mud.

An eerie green light shone around him and he feared being captured by the enemy. He looked up to see an angel bending over him.

"Sargento! Sargento! Are you going to be all right?" she asked breathlessly, while trying to help him up.

Joe couldn't breathe, let alone stand.

Louise must have realized the problem. "Try to relax," she said. Then she placed her mouth over his, her hand over his nose to force air into his oxygen starved lungs.

Joe coughed, sputtered, finally beginning to breathe on his own. He moaned. "I feel like I've been run over by a train." He hurt all over, his breathing was labored and he was thankful for her knee under his head holding it out of the mud and the filthy water.

Gabby knelt down beside the girl and quickly examined him. He had been hit in both legs by shrapnel. He also had a bullet hole through the bottom of his left foot. Fortunately, the bullet had exited just below the ankle. The leg wounds were bleeding profusely. Using a pressure bandage, Gabby worked feverishly trying to stop the bleeding. Joe looked down, rather relieved to find out it was blood wetting his trousers and not the other. He preferred pain instead of embarrassment. He wanted Louise to think of him as a man, not a scared kid.

He had come close to dying. Looking down at his wounds, Joe said, "Do you happen to have a Medic available? I don't think I'll be walking far without one." He closed his eyes. Why had he agreed to come here? What had he gotten himself into at this 'Bay of Pigs'?

"Let me look at you," Louise said. "Your legs are soaked with blood. We have a first aid kit. Let's try to get the bleeding stopped."

"Not now. We'd better find cover in a hurry. If they saw that plane get hit, they'll be coming to see if anything is left after the crash. We can look at my wounds later. Just help me out of this water."

Louise and Gabby pulled him from the water and helped him to his feet.

Joe gritted his teeth with pain, determined to make it back on his own two feet. "Have you found a place to set up a camp that doesn't show from the air?" he asked.

Louise nodded in the affirmative as she pointed and said, "This way."

Joe checked his carbine for damage and found that the sniper scope had been dislodged from his weapon and damaged in the fall, but it was still working well enough for him to scan the area. There didn't seem to be any movement anywhere, so they headed for the encampment. A trio of the men who had been gathering the bundles had remained behind to see if the US Sargento had made it alive. They had kept the fire going.

That small fire was a welcome sight to Joe when they got back to the temporary sanctuary.

"Gabby, get those field pants off of him," Louise ordered and she gently washed his injured legs. Fresh water was at a premium so they had to strain swamp water through a cloth to screen out some of the impurities. She boiled some of the water. She used it to wash his wounds and she used the rest to rinse the blood out of his trousers.

Louise turned to Gabby and said, "Get the liquor. We'll use it to sterilize and cauterize these wounds. Hurry! His right leg won't stop bleeding."

The men held Joe down as she poured some of the rum into his wounds. It burned like fire. The raw alcohol caused more pain than the bullets had. It was all Joe could do to keep from screaming out in pain.

She said, "That should help to keep the infection down."

Gabby reached into the fire and picked up a burning twig. He touched it to the wound, igniting the alcohol with a flash. The flames raced through the open wounds with a searing pain. Joe fought them, but the men continued to hold him down.

"Let go of me," he yelled. "My legs are on fire." As the burning subsided, the men released him and he fell back with a sigh, exhausted and in shock. "Why didn't you just douse me with gasoline and set me afire?"

"Not have some gas," Gabby said with a mischievous grin.

"It's for your own good, Sargento," Louise said kindly. "I know it hurts, but it must be done or infection would kill you. I'll wrap your upper right thigh first because it was hurt the worst."

"You should save some of that first aid stuff for later," he panted, still in pain from the treatment.

"If we lose you, there won't be any later. You are our only hope." Her hands were rough, but her touch was gentle as she applied the dressing.

Oh great, what is this world coming to? he thought. The future of Cuba is in my shaky hands.

"You've done this before, haven't you?" Joe asked.

"Yes, many times," she said. "It's not uncommon to have one of our people beaten up, or shot by the Federalist troops. We do what we must."

"You do good work." He slowly pulled his pants on, careful not to knock the bandages off.

"Thank you kind, sir," she said. "Anytime."

Joe hoped there wouldn't be another time. Picking up his weapon, he saw it was full of mud and sand from its dunking in the swamp. He stripped off the damaged sniper scope, then cleaned it the best he could. Louise traded him guns because she didn't completely understand how to use the scope on her rifle.

Gabby went looking for Joe's rucksack and found it near the impact area. It had fallen hard and most of his ammunition had been submerged in the dark water of the swamp. Louise and Gabby seemed to be more in control than Joe. This was their country and he had the disadvantage of being a foreigner. He was not used to such a miserable environment. They had been living in the swamp for several weeks, awaiting his arrival and knew their way around. Sergeant Joe, on the other hand, had no idea where he was.

"You must have been under that plane when I came out of it. You found me so fast," Joe said.

"We have been waiting and watching for you. You were late, so we think maybe you not coming, but here you are," she spoke happily.

"Yes, here I am," Joe said soberly.

"We have to get to the main camp," Gabby said.

"Can you walk now, Sargento?" Louise asked

"I'll try. Let's get moving." Joe stood to his feet. After his ordeal with the fire, his legs hurt so much that he figured that walking couldn't hurt much more. It was late at night and so dark that it was almost impossible to see your hand in front of your face. Try as he might, he couldn't see a thing as they moved into the trees.

Louise walked in front of Joe, taking the lead. "Follow me closely. Gabby, you bring up the rear so the Sargento not get lost. He doesn't know his way around this place."

Startled by an animal, the little party froze in their tracks, remaining motionless for some time. This tactic Joe understood. The natives had taught him to remain motionless for hours. They did not have to wait long before Louise motioned them on. He tried to keep up with her as she went through the underbrush. He found himself being hit in the face by small branches with just about every step.

He said, "Hey, take it easy. I can't see a thing." It was even darker as they moved through the trees. The dense canopy of foliage blocked what light might have come from the stars. A little moonlight would have made the going much easier.

Joe thought about his co-workers at home and his boss, Mack. They were probably in some bar, cozy and warm. He pushed the thought aside. He had to concentrate on the mission and nothing else. He needed to stay mentally alert.

The pungent smell of stagnant water, dead fish, and rotting vegetation was strong, along with the lingering odor of burnt flesh. It was almost more than he could endure. They were unfamiliar smells and made him feel sick and afraid. Other aromas filled the night air. Many types of fauna and flora lent their scent to the potpourri in the blackness.

Then there were the sounds of the swamp at night. Strange sounds. Frightening sounds. Unseen critters slithered across the trail. He couldn't see them, but he could feel them brush up against him. Off in the distance a bullfrog croaked a love song to his ladylove. Joe could hear something splashing around in the dark water nearby. By the sound of the slap on the water, he surmised that it was something big. Perhaps a crocodile or an alligator, or whatever reptile species lived there. He hoped what he heard wasn't a snake. He gave a shudder.

He had a thing about snakes. He had read about phobias and figured he had one when it came to snakes. All snakes, not just the poisonous kind. He wasn't afraid of lions and tigers and bears (Oh, my). Yet, the thought of a creepy snake, big or small, would send a chill up his spine. He remembered how he had walked blocks out of his way to avoid a pet shop that kept a snake cage in the window.

Joe wondered if there were animal predators in the swamp that would attack a man, especially one with the smell of fresh blood on him. Determined not to let his fears taunt him, he made up his mind to ignore them. He was the American sergeant sent here to help these people. He was a man and he must act like one. Besides, Louise and Gabby didn't seem to be the slightest bit scared as they trudged through knee-deep ooze, zigzagging their way through the growth of water plants.

They walked until they came to a place where the ground was a bit higher and considerably dryer. Suddenly, Louise stopped, causing Joe to bump into her. She almost fell forward, but he caught her by the arm steadying her. He looked ahead at a small fire glowing near the center of the clearing. It was a welcome sight and made him feel a bit more at ease.

When they got to the camp, he sat down on the damp sand, removed his boots and took off his wet, heavy army socks. Louise sat down by him and silently pointed to the leeches on his legs. Horrified, Joe started to pull the leeches off.

Louise grabbed his hand, shaking her head. "Wait, we have some salt that will bring the little critters out. If you pull them out, the heads stay in and they become infected." She poured a little salt into a cup of water and sprinkled the solution on the leeches on their legs. The little repulsive things detached themselves. By that time, some of the men had begun to filter in from the woods. Joe didn't know where they had been hiding or where they were coming from. The men seemed to materialize out of nowhere. They could move through that muddy place without making a sound. Joe thought they must have been born and raised in the swamp. They knew their way around. With water all around them, the group had a hard time finding a dry place to sit.

Joe began to take a headcount as Louise introduced each man when they came into the camp. "Sargento, do you remember Sam, Ben and Smoky?" Each man had a code name or nickname that he went by. If any of them were captured by the National Army of Cuba and made to talk, he couldn't reveal what he didn't know. They feared that the NAC would take reprisals against the families of the rebels.

Much to his chagrin, the sergeant couldn't remember half of their names and they all looked alike to him. Louise knew all of them and promised to help him out until he became more familiar with them.

One of the rebels drew Joe aside. "Hello, Mr. Big Shot, American Sargento. Remember me?" Carlos asked bitterly. "I know something about you that you don't think I do."

"Is that right?" Joe asked.

"You bet. You think she's for you, but she's mine."

"Do you mean Louise?" Joe felt amused.

"You see, you don't even know her real name, but I know everything about her. I know her all her life." He hesitated thoughtfully and then plunged dangerously ahead. "Marcia Cordona is her real name. Did you know that her mother used to work as a domestic, also English interpreter for Batista? Did you know her mother came from America? That's how she speaks English so good. Her father used to be a big shot lawyer in Havana before Castro took over. Did you know that, Mr. American Sargento? Did you know that her father and my father were amigos and that her father promise her to me when we both babies."

"That's enough!" Joe snapped. "I don't need to know so much about her. If I get captured, I might be forced to tell them her real name. You know that is a breech of security. If you cared about her, you would protect her identity. You're just being spiteful. Now get back to your post before I forget you're on our side. I'm making you a promise. If you cause her to get hurt, I'll hunt you down and shoot you!" Joe pulled back the bolt on the rifle and let it slide a round into the chamber. "I should go ahead and shoot you for this."

Carlos glared at Joe, his black eyes like inkwells. "You not scare me," he said before he turned and stalked out of the clearing.

Joe watched him go, thinking I had better keep an eye on this fellow. He's big trouble. He didn't have time to give Carlos more then a passing thought because he had a job to do. He called out to Louise.

"Come over here near the fire light so we can look over that map. Gabby, you come with her. I'd like your opinion on a couple of things." He stopped and listened. "Hold it," he ordered. "Douse the fire, I hear a plane."

Before anyone could comply, the obsolete WWII vintage B-26 Bomber came in low and slow, just above the treetops. It began circling over their hiding place with its landing lights on. Joe hoped it planned to make a supply drop. He caught Gabby's hand to prevent him from displaying the red and green landing lights. This was the exiles' main camp and he couldn't take the chance of giving away their position. Even if it were a friendly, it would be a leak in security. He thought about opening fire on the tattletale aircraft, but he knew that the sound of ground fire would be a dead giveaway to any enemies in the area.

Joe knew the plane might be old and outdated, but she still carried lots of firepower in her fifty-caliber guns. He ordered all hands to lay low. That plane just wouldn't go away.

The men doused the fire and made for the cover of the swamp.

"They're looking for the plane that brought me in," Joe said.

"They won't find it because it's all in little pieces," Louise answered.

After some time the search plane moved on to another search pattern, leaving the little band of rebels alone in the solitude of the darkness. The men quickly rekindled the fire and everyone stood near it trying to dry off their clothing. The map had been forgotten for the moment.

CHAPTER TWELVE

Joe spent some time learning to find his way around the little camp. He saw Louise and Gabby way ahead of him. Tagging along behind, he could hear angry voices.

They seemed to be having a disagreement. It was too dark to see them and they were speaking Spanish, but by the tone of their voices, it was clear they were in a heated argument.

Catching up to them, Joe saw Gabby shake Louise, apparently trying to push her along the path they had just come down.

Joe pulled Gabby away from the girl. "Take your hands off of her! We don't fight women where I come from. What's going on here, Louise? Do you want me to shoot him?" The carbine went into the port arms position as Joe waited for her to agree.

"No, Sargento!" she said with alarm. "He not hurt me. He good friend, please you not shoot at him."

"Well, all right, but let's not have friction among ourselves. We'll have enough fighting to do in a little while," Joe said, wondering what they were fighting about.

It's a good thing they didn't call my bluff, Joe thought. I couldn't have shot anybody, and for sure not Gabby.

Gabby motioned to Joe, wanting to tell him something. The man pointed in the direction Joe thought might be Havana. "Her go away! Stay here, no good! Not good!"

Louise, her dark eyes sparkling with anger, grabbed a burning branch from the fire taking off after Gabby. She chased him all over the camp before she gave up on catching him. She threw the branch back into the fire. Clinching her tiny fist, she said, "Not your business if I stay here. Leave me alone."

Gabby walked away, hearing the chuckles of his compatriots, his face red, shaking his head. "No good. No good," he grumbled. "Better she go."

"He's right, Louise," Joe said. "If you have a place you can go, you should. This is a dangerous place for anyone, especially a woman."

"I stay with you," she said. "I want to help. I not want to go away."

Joe tried to reason with her. "I think it's time you left. You've done your duty. You have been a big help, but we can manage now." Joe might not admit it, but he was afraid something might happen to her.

"You can't make me go. I stay," she replied stubbornly, stomping her foot defiantly and looking as if she might cry.

"All right, you can stay a little longer, but you'll have to leave soon," Joe said, but in his heart, he knew it would be impossible for him to do his job without her. She was his interpreter and the men didn't know enough English to understand him. He didn't know but a few words of Spanish. Louise was the link that held the chain together. Without her, the mission would fail. '

"How did you clear out this place?" he asked, just to change the subject. "I can tell that someone has done quite a lot of work here. How'd you manage it, right under the enemy's nose?"

"We not clear. Carboneros do it."

"Carboneros? What's a Carbonero?" Joe asked.

"Carboneros make charcoal from trees and brush and sell it for a living." She sat down beside Joe, her anger abated. "For most of the people who live in the swamp, that's the only work they have, cutting wood and burning it to make charcoal. They must carry it out of this place, mostly on their backs. It's very hard work."

"It sounds like a difficult way to make a living," Joe said, listening as she explained the ways of the people.

"They all work, the whole family, even the small children, to add a few centavos (pennies) to their income. Even the old ones have to work by carrying little bundles of wood to make a fire. They also get their food by fishing and hunting the wild game in the swamp. It is not easy for them to live on so little," she said. "That's why there aren't many people living in the Septa swamplands."

Joe felt sorry for the people. He had grown up poor, but compared to these people he probably was wealthy living in the States. His conversation with Louise came to an abrupt halt when Gabby came back into camp bleeding from a cut on the back of his leg.

"How did that happen?" Joe asked, not understanding a word Gabby said.

"The root of a mahogany tree cut him. They very sharp," Louise explained as she took the first aid kit from her pack and went over to him. She handed it to the injured man, then walked back to the fire without helping Gabby as she had helped Joe.

Curious, he asked her, "Why don't you help that man fix his wound?"

"He know what do," she said indifferently. "I need stay with you. Help you make orders. Our friends will help him."

"Are you still mad at him?"

"He wants to be my boss, but I'm staying here to help you with the soldiers." She flipped her hair over her shoulder and eyed Joe speculatively.

"Well, don't stay mad at him when he was only looking out for you. That makes him my very good friend, so go make up with him. Do it now!" he commanded. "While you're there, help him with that cut. Can I rely on you to be a good soldier?" Joe asked, appealing to her patriotic side.

She nodded in the affirmative. "I fix him good."

"I don't want him getting an infection in that thing and I can't have two of my best soldiers fighting. Do I make myself clear?" he growled in a threatening tone, working hard to suppress a laugh.

"I am a good soldier," she said as she walked over to where Gabby was trying to clean his own wound.

"I never doubted that for a minute," Joe said to her retreating back. He caught Gabby's eye and gave him a wink and a grin. The lad smiled back.

"I sorry I hate you so much." She knelt down to help Gabby. "I don't do what you tell me, so Sargento yell at me. Now I fix your tiny little scratch for you. Try not to cry too much."

Joe knew what Gabby was in for and felt grateful that she had been in a better mood when she had worked on him. He didn't envy Gabby one bit. Soon the cut was cleaned and dressed. Gabby looked over at the sergeant as she finished her mission of mercy and returned his wink and grin.

Joe had watched the procedure and felt sorry for Gabby. He thought she had scrubbed a little harder than was necessary and when she poured on the aqua vitae, he thought he noticed just a bit of satisfaction on her face. Still the deed was done and the two of them had made up.

"Have the men come in," Joe said. "Pass the word. We'll need to know what kind of ordinance we have to work with and have them bring all the weapons we have. I want to see a tally sheet of all the ammunition available. I'll need to know how we stand and how to deploy our firepower. As you all know our job is to provide covering fire for the paratroopers and helicopters as they come in."

"We'll break the men down into four teams of ten. Tell them to leave two men on guard at each section. We need guards posted at all times."

Louise trudged through the water and mud without making a sound. Soon she had spread the word to all the men. Silently they came in from the swamp. It amazed him that the men moved so quietly. If he hadn't seen them with his own eyes, he would have sworn that there was nobody out there. Their feet made sucking sounds in the mud as they came in, but you had to listen hard to hear it. He supposed it was the background noise of the swamp that helped to camouflage their movements, but Joe also understood the men were well trained. With help from Louise, he asked their names and what their jobs were.

The first group was mortar men, but they had only one launcher and it was a small 60-mm. Their mortar bombs had been damaged in the airdrop. The tail fins were bent out of shape. That would make them highly unreliable. It would be very doubtful that they could hit a target.

"Just how much undamaged ammo do you have?" Joe asked, instinctively dreading the answer.

"Only twenty-seven bombs," Louise answered.

"That'll make our job a lot harder," he said. "Do you have a good position for your mortar emplacement?"

The men looked puzzled.

"Never mind, we will look at it in the morning when the sun comes up. How about small arms? What do they have and how much ammo?" Joe asked Louise.

"We have a fifty cal machine-gun with 1,000 rounds of ammo."

"That isn't much ammo for a fire fight," he said. "How many barrels do you have for it?"

"Just one, some of the ammo and the other two barrels were lost out there somewhere," she said, pointing out toward the wetlands. "Will that a problem?"

"You bet it's a problem," he said, anger in his voice. "We'll only be able to fire short bursts. If we stay on it too long, the barrel will melt down. Where are the rest of the supplies we asked for? What happened to them? I can't believe that they would send us out here without the proper equipment to fight with. How many radios do we have?"

"Just one, but we have extra batteries for it." Louise tried to assure him. "It not matter much because we can't use it if we're to maintain radio silence."

"That's true, but we can listen," Joe reminded her. "We might get some information on what the bad guys are up to and maybe find out what's happening with the assault on the beaches. Louise, I'll need you to be my ears so stay with the radio. You'll need to check in on them as much as you can. The US troops will speak in English, but it'll be the Spanish that tells us what we'll need to know. You can listen in and tell me how everything is going. If you hear any English, I want you to write it down and bring it to me immediately."

She gave him a sort of two-fingered Girl Scout salute. "Yes, sir."

With no small effort, he swallowed the smile that threatened to spread across his lips. The other three groups came in for the meeting with their US commander. Joe tried to get some kind of an idea as to what they had to work with and who, if anyone, knew what was expected of them.

"Louise, can you make a list of what we have and try to make a map of the way it's deployed? Where is the mortar emplacement located? In addition, I want to know where every foxhole is and who is in it. We might need to find them in the dark. If the unthinkable happens, we'll know who got hit. Tell the men to keep on digging through the night. I hate to keep all of them up, but those holes will have to be deep. We just might need them at first light. We'd better be as ready as we can. Please remember to write the information in English, so I can read it."

"Will you want anything else, Sargento?" Louise looked up at him with serious black eyes, the pad poised in her hand.

"Yeah, two tickets home," he said with a grin.

"Two tickets?" Louise asked, her eyes twinkling.

"Of course, two. You don't think I'd leave you here, do you?" Joe said, trying to work up a scowl. "Let's get down to business. We can dream later."

He looked over at the men digging the holes. "Tell the men to put rocks and logs and anything else they can find into the dirt around the tops of their fox holes. Loose dirt won't stop a bullet. Tell them to cover their pit with fresh branches each morning. That red earth can be seen a mile away, in the air. Make the holes deeper at one end. If a grenade lands in the hole with them, they can kick it into that hole. At least they'll have a chance. Louise, tell them I'm not looking for heroes. Just try to stay alive."

"You really care about these men, don't you, Sargento?" she remarked. "They need sleep. They have not rested for two days. Do you think we could take a short break for a little sleep?"

He was so busy that he hadn't noticed the tired lines around her eyes and mouth. "How about you?" he asked. "How long have you been awake?"

She shrugged. "I don't remember."

"How many men do we have all together?" Joe asked.

"We have forty-four men and me," she said proudly. "I make forty-five."

"So you do." If she knew how important she was to the mission, she never let on. He knew she would not sleep if the men were ordered to work. She looked as if she was staying awake by pure will power. "Tell them to put two men in each fox hole. One will watch while the other works. Tell them to share the work fairly. I'm sure Castro's men have seen the plane dropping supplies. They'll know we're here somewhere and that we are up to something. They will be coming to investigate. How long until daybreak?" Joe asked.

"From the looks of the sky," she said looking into the dark void above her head, "it'll be soon."

"Maybe some of us can get a little sleep in the morning." He looked at the tired, hunched shoulders of the men digging nearby. "We won't need as many sentries in the daylight because we can see them coming. Tell the men to keep digging. We will try to get a little rest at daybreak. Remember, one awake and one asleep. That way half the troops can sleep at a time. If we can make it through the night, we'll be okay. We're in too much danger at night. That road is full of traffic and some of them may be the enemy. Keep your eyes open and be as quiet as possible. Be careful not to fire on your own people. Make sure they are military targets. Remember that we are not to engage unless we have to defend ourselves. We're only here to secure a spot for airborne troops when they arrive. Louise, come with me. Let's see how the men are doing."

"Are you sure, Sargento?" she asked. "Your legs are not healed and they could start bleeding again."

"I am not here to be pampered," Joe said gruffly. "I'm here to look after you and your people, not to have you baby me."

As they walked from place to place, Joe could feel his feet sinking into that black, stinking mud. It took a great deal of hard work to make much headway. The mire kept pulling at his jump boots and the pain in his legs increased with each step. The throbbing in his head was so severe that he could barely think. "Louise, do you have any more aspirin in the kit?"

"Yes, but they have gotten wet from the moisture in the air and are all crumbled up. Gabby has lots of that rum." She could tell that every step was an effort for Joe, so she retraced her footsteps taking hold of his arm to try to help him.

"I can't afford to drink that stuff. I'll have to keep a clear head. Tell Gabby not to drink it either," he ordered, gritting his teeth with pain. "On second thought, tell him to bring it by and I will try a little of it along with some of the aspirin paste."

Just then, Gabby came along with his small pack still on his back and a battered old guitar slung over his shoulder. A scabbard containing a large knife hung from his belt. Louise spoke to him in Spanish. Gabby took one look at Joe, reached into his backpack, pulling out a dark green glass bottle. He handed it to Joe, who took a healthy swig to wash down the nasty tasting aspirin crumbs. Joe handed it back to Gabby gasping. It burned his throat, but at the same time, produced a numbing effect that felt good.

"Thanks. I needed that if I am to continue. I think that will help as soon as the aspirin takes effect. We can't waste any time. We'd better start looking in on our defensive positions."

Just then, the old B-26 came back, the sound of the engines cutting through the night. He was flying lower then before, barely missing the treetops, and as before, he had his landing lights on. Thinking they may have wanted to drop them some more supplies, Gabby turned on his flashlight and signaled the plane.

"Shut that thing off!" Joe shouted. "We don't know who that is up there. It could be some of Castro's boys." He snatched the light from Gabby's hand. "Louise, get on the radio and see if you can find them on the airwaves. They know our frequency so they should respond if they are friendly."

"The radio is over on the other side of the camp. They'll be gone before I can get over there," Louise said.

"You had better hurry then," he said.

Louise looked up into the gray sky. "Look. He has seen Gabby's light. Look, here he comes."

"Get undercover," Joe ordered, ushering them toward the trees. "They could start shooting. Those planes carry quite a bit of firepower. Gabby, I hope your light doesn't get us killed."

The plane passed over them like a great lumbering giant, giving no indication that he had seen the light. It was just flying in wide circles with those accursed landing lights on, as if searching for something, but giving away the store in the process. They had made two passes overhead and were coming back around for the third, when a fighter jet came in low and fast, just over the tree tops. The jet was moving so rapidly that he overshot the slower, bigger plane by a mile. Making a wide turn, he returned screaming back to attack, guns blazing and flaps down. The old bomber took several hits from what sounded like fifty-caliber machine gunfire. They watched as the big B-26 jettisoned some of its cargo. In the half-light, they couldn't tell if they were bombs or supplies. When the objects didn't explode, Joe sent for Mike and with some help from Louise, sent him to check it out. "Don't go alone. Find a partner to go with you. And keep out of sight," Joe ordered.

The old plane turned southeast and headed in the direction of the sea. It struggled to maintain altitude. It managed to stay above the trees. They weren't firing back at the aggressor. The gunfire from the speedy little jet was taking its toll on the larger plane.

As they watched they could see pieces of metal falling from the crippled bomber as it tried to make good its escape. All they could do was watch helplessly as the sleek fighter jet cut the gallant old warrior to pieces. She struggled to stay in the air, but it soon became apparent that the old bird was losing the battle. Smoke billowing from one of her engines, she gave up her last ditch attempt to stay in the air, going down a short distance from where the guerrillas were hiding.

Louise listened to the radio and gave a blow-by-blow account of the action as it took place. "They are calling, Mayday! Mayday!" she said. "They must be Americanos because they are speaking English. It looks like our help was coming. The big plane is one of ours and it has been shot down," she reported breathlessly. "Can't we help them?"

"We can't spare more than a couple of men to check it out. I don't think that they have a snowball's chance, but let's try." Joe knew the enemy would be all over that plane. "This will be a job for volunteers only. Do any of you want to go?" Louise interpreted for them.

To Joe's amazement, just about all of them stepped forward, willing even knowing the risk involved. "I'll go too, Sargento Joe," Louise insisted. "They're American and I can talk to them."

Joe chose two men, Sam and Pat. He believed he was sending them to an early grave. "Louise, I need you here. They can scout out the place and see if there are any survivors. Tell them to be careful. I don't want them captured or killed."

"But, Sargento, they speak hardly any English. Someone will need to talk to these Americanas," she insisted, her proud chin lifted.

"You may be right," Joe answered. How could he argue with her? If they were Americanos, it was his duty to rescue them. "Okay, Sam and Pat will stay here. They can help with the placement of the troops. Sam, you help Gabby. He will be in charge of the group until we get back. Don't take chances. Stay alive. We can't win a war with dead soldiers."

"Louise and I will go. I hope that we'll attract less attention and stand a better chance of getting through. I'd like to know just what that plane was carrying and see if anyone survived the crash," Joe said, hoping to find the men alive.

Everything that Joe stated was true, but he had an ulterior motive. He wanted to protect Louise and to keep her by his side. "Tell them that it may take us awhile. We'll watch the plane for a time to make sure it isn't a trap. When we're sure, we'll move in. That jet will have radioed in their position to the enemy and they'll be out searching for it."

"You be careful and watchful, Sargento. We not want you to get captured. They'll shoot you on the spot," Gabby told him, with Louise interpreting for him.

116

Joe slapped Gabby on the back. "We'll be careful. Be watching for us. We'll come back for help if there's anything to salvage, but I imagine it is a total loss. If by chance there is anything left, we will bring back anything we can carry and hide anything we have to leave behind. If any of the crew are still alive, they'll need help."

Joe shouted out orders. "Louise, bring the first aid kit with you, and Gabby, do you have any of that rum left? Give us one of those small bottles just in case one of us gets a cut or something. That's the only medicine we have. If anyone lived through that crash, they'll need all the assistance we can give them. If we need help, we will wave my white tee shirt from a tall tree, so watch for it with the scope. Keep your heads down and we'll be back as soon as we can. We'll take two of the carbines, we may have to move fast, and they'll be much easier to handle than the M-1s if we have to make a run for it."

"Shouldn't you take at least one M-1 rifle?" suggested Gabby. "They have a lot more range and a great deal more fire power."

"We're going to try to avoid a fire fight," Joe said. "The carbines are only for self defense. If we do find anything on the plane, we can carry it more easily if we don't have to lug those heavy Garands."

Just then, Mike came running into camp with his partner following close behind. "They beat us to the drop," he shouted. "The NAC got there before us. It was food, cans of water and what looked like some M-14s. Now they have it all. I'm sorry, Sargento. We went as fast as we could, but we were too late."

Joe couldn't let his disappointment show. It might demoralize the men. "You did the best you could. There isn't anything more you could've done. You both did a fine job. I am proud of you…for that matter I'm proud of all of you."

Early dawn began to make its way across the dark sky. "It's coming daylight," he said. "We'd better take a look at how the defensive positions are set up, before we check on the plane." With Louise leading the way, Joe followed close behind her to avoid falling into one of the foxholes. They moved swiftly through the trees; at the edge of the road they came across the mortar emplacement. They had chosen just the right spot.

The 60-mm Mortar had a range of 1000 to 1985 yards. They had dug in on the backside of the little hill under the branches of a large tree. That would give them cover from the air, making them harder to see from the ground.

"You couldn't have chosen a better place," he told the crew. "You have a commanding field of fire that covers the road and the far hillside. Great job guys. It's good to work with men who know what they are doing."

"Thank you, Sargento. We can wipe them out from here. I show you," said Loco, with a toothless grin. He sent a dummy round down range. It went up through the foliage disappearing into the predawn sky, then landed with a "Plink", smack in the middle of the road.

"Good shooting," Joe said. "That makes me glad that you're on our side."

"I can do again." The gunner dropped another round down the tube. It was a direct hit right in the middle of the road.

"How long have you been using that road as a target?" Joe had to ask.

"All night and most of morning," he said. "Those bad bombs are good for something."

"Do you see that tree with the broken limb? When they get even with that tree, let 'em have it," Joe said and the gunner nodded. He inspected one of the foxholes. "This hole needs to be a bit deeper and dig a deep hole in one end of it like I told you last night. If a grenade comes into the hole, it should roll into the pit. Then when it goes off, most of the blast will go straight up and you just might get to keep all of your fingers and toes." Though he was serious, the men laughed.

"Come on, Louise. Let's go and see if anyone survived that crash." As Louise and Joe walked through the camp, she said, "You've made friends of all these people. There isn't a man among them who wouldn't lay down his life for you, Sargento...me too."

"I certainly hope that won't be necessary." Joe's voice sounded husky. The thought of this young, beautiful girl losing her life to save his hide totally went against all he believed in. The boy saves the girl. He had watched enough movies to know the story line. Besides, the feelings he had for Louise were new to him. He had been with girls before, but he had never worried about what might happen to them. With Louise, it was different. "The idea is to make the other fellow give up his life and I've grown quite fond of all of you."

CHAPTER THIRTEEN

When Joe and Louise started walking toward the plane, Gabby came running behind them. "I want to go with you. You'll need help if anyone is alive over there."

"No, my friend." Joe shook his head. "I want you to look after things here until we get back. Make sure that the mortar emplacement is ready to go when we need it. Louise and I will come back for help if we need you, but first I want to scout out the place. I don't want to lead any of you into a trap."

"Sargento, can we get started now?" Louise inquired.

"All right, let's get going. Empty two of those packs and bring them along in case we find anything we can use," he said.

Placing the empty packs on their backs, they headed in the direction of the downed aircraft. Looking for the safest way to get there without being seen, they followed the road, but kept close to the tree line. They walked in the brush as much as possible. They had only traveled about a mile and a half, when some of Castro's henchmen came roaring by. They were headed in the direction of the beach, where the 2506th Combat team would be coming ashore. They were so sure of winning the battle that they weren't looking around for enemies. Instead, the men were drinking, laughing and having a high old time.

Joe and Louise stepped into the brush just in time to avoid being seen by the first scout car. He followed so close to Louise that when she pulled the low branches apart and let them go, Joe got hit in the face. 'Swat'. It happened again. 'Swat'.

"Hey, watch it, will you?" he said. "That hurt."

"Sorry, Sargento. You shouldn't be so close behind me."

"I can't help it. I worry that if we get separated in the swamp, we might never find each other again. The grass and weeds are so high, it would be easy to get lost out here and I have no prior experience in a swamp. I'll stay far enough behind to keep from being slapped in the face, but slow down and give me a chance to keep up with you."

Spotting a large tree, they waded out to it. The roots of the larger trees tended to form small islands around them, so they hid themselves behind the soggy mound. The convoy picked that very spot to stop for a break so the men could relieve themselves. It was about fifty yards from where Joe and Louise were hiding. Shouting and laughing, the soldiers bragged about what they would do to the foreign invaders if they got their hands on them.

Louise slipped, accidentally letting go of the limb she held, causing it to whip back with a whooshing noise. Some of the Cuban soldiers looked their way and started firing into the water and brush.

Joe and Louise huddled behind the tree as bullets whizzed by them and kicked up mud only inches from their heads. They stayed as low as they could with their heads barely above the water. If the enemy soldiers spotted them, there would be no place to run. He held his index finger up to his lips as a signal for her to be quiet. She grinned and covered her mouth with her hand. Joe had scraped his leg on a root, but that was the least of his worries. A hail of bullets crackled and snapped all around them, knocking bits of wood from the tree and making plunking sounds in the water.

Louise flinched and stiffened in fear and pain. She gave out a little cry. It came involuntarily from her throat but was so low that if he hadn't been within inches of her, he wouldn't have heard it.

"I'm shot!" she said with shock and surprise.

"Where are you hit?" he asked in a low voice.

"Not sure," she replied nervously. "You'll have to leave me and go on alone. I'm hurt too bad to keep up."

"I'm not leaving you in a place like this and that is the last I want to hear of it," Joe whispered angrily above her ear.

"Sargento, you were right. I'm just in the way," she whimpered.

He worried that Louise would get hysterical. What a time for her to lose control with the Cubans breathing down their necks. "Knock it off," he rebuked her sternly, even though he barely whispered the words. "You are not in the way. I couldn't do my job without you and you know it. Besides…I love you."

Her eyes grew wide as she looked at Joe. "I…I…Me too, Sargento." Her eyes looked troubled. "You're just saying that because I'm hurt."

He smiled down at her and kissed her lips, which were barely above water. Our first real kiss, he thought. It would be one they would always remember and one that they could tell their grandchildren about. How many people could recall their first kiss and say that it was when they were immersed in black, muddy water up to their necks with Cuban soldiers shooting at them?

Joe felt he had let her down... she was so young. He was her commander, and having a romance in a war torn country could compromise their safety. The time might come when she would have to leave him to save herself. He would expect it of her. Even command her to leave him in spite of the fact that he knew he could never leave her. He needed to get her to safety. He didn't see any blood in the water, but that didn't mean anything with all the scummy mud that had been disturbed by their movements. She could bleed to death if they didn't get it treated. As quietly as possible, trying hard not to make a sound, he began swimming backward with an arm around her waist. Silently, he pulled her to a small clearing behind a tree. All thoughts of the downed plane had left him. His mission now was her safety. He didn't know what to expect. She had been hit by a thirty caliber round and they could really do some damage. Joe pulled her to a low mound of earth that was barely above the water line. Satisfied that they could not be seen from the road, he lifted her up and placed her on it. He crawled onto the mound and lay beside her, holding her close, trying to shield her with his own body. He held her until her trembling subsided.

"Am I going to die?" she whispered softly.

"No, I won't let you leave me now that I have found you. I can't tell how bad it is until I have a chance to see where you're hit," he whispered. "It might not be all that bad."

Not being able to raise his head for fear of being detected, he started going over her body with his hands, feeling for the wound.

"Be brave and don't move," he told her. "They can't stay there much longer. At least they've stopped shooting."

Just then, one of the soldiers shouted, "It must have been an animal. Save your bullets for the worms on the beach." They climbed back into their trucks, but sat there waiting for orders to move out toward the fighting.

"We've got to find out where you're hit." He worried she might lose too much blood. They were far from a hospital or transfusions. "Can you feel it? Where did they get you?"

"I don't know. My whole body feels numb." She lay face down on the mound of dirt and began to cry softly.

He gently ran his hand over her body, desperately trying to locate the bullet hole.

She sobbed. "My right leg or hip, I think."

Gently searching along her leg, he couldn't find anything wrong. Moving his fingertips up the outside of her leg and hip, he found a small hole in her bottom, just below the hip pocket. She flinched as his hand passed over the wound.

"I've found it, but you'll have to pull these down so that I can get a look at that wound. I won't look anymore than I need to," he promised.

She hesitated before she undid her belt and pushed her pants down.

Immediately, he found the small flesh wound, about one inch in length and not more than an eighth of an inch deep. If it had been one inch to the right, she would have lost a big chunk of her backside. Glad to find she had only a minor mishap, he felt like laughing. However, the joy was replaced with the realization that in this hostile environment, even a scratch could be fatal. There was always the threat of infection and there was no medication to fight it, nothing but the rum.

"I'm going to have to clean that thing up. It's going to hurt some."

"How bad is it?" she moaned.

"I've seen worse. He just nicked your fanny."

"Will it leave a bad scar?" she asked, ever mindful of the one on her chin.

"I wouldn't worry about it. It doesn't look that bad to me. However, I do think that we should patch this up before the numbness wears off. It will hurt like crazy then."

"Okay, I'm ready." She gritted her teeth. "Lets get this over with so I can put my clothes back on."

He opened the first aid kit, taking out a piece of gauze to swab the wound. He poured on a bit of the rum and dabbed the cut. She whispered a string of words that made him glad he didn't understand Spanish. He wondered if she was cursing out his ancestors. They heard shouting from the soldiers as they departed in a cloud of exhaust smoke.

He applied a waterproof bandage. "Get dressed. I think you are going to live." Joe couldn't hold back a little chuckle, releasing the fear and tension that had built up inside him.

Louise looked at him as though he had gone out of his mind. What could be funny about her being shot? Her dark eyes snapping with anger, she said, "You make fun of me? I hurt and you laughing! Why you not like me anymore? Do you like to see me hurt?" She said a few more things in Spanish that he didn't understand, but he got their meaning all right.

Joe stopped laughing long enough to pull her close to him. "I'm not making fun of you. I would never do that. I'm so relieved that you are okay. I just couldn't help it. I was so afraid you'd been hurt real bad." He smiled at her. "Someday you might see the humor in this. Not now, I guess," he admitted, as she frowned at him. "Pull up your drawers and lets see if you can stand on your feet."

As she pulled her trousers up, she cringed as they passed over the cut. Not able to get to her feet, she sat up.

"I should never have let you come with me. You might have gotten your butt shot off." Joe began to laugh again. This time she smiled.

"You fix me up real good, Sargento. I don't care that you laugh, now I know that you really do care about me."

After an hour, she began to move her toes, then her foot and soon she had the full use of her leg. She was just beginning to feel the effects of the bullet. He helped her to stand. She leaned on him until she was able to walk on her own. As the feeling came back into her leg, the wound began to burn.

"Louise, I am so proud of you. I know that bullet hole must have hurt like crazy, but you acted like a good soldier."

"I am good soldier," she told him, standing as tall as she could. "I'm more afraid of being captured by those men, than that little pain. I have pain before, this nothing new to me."

Limping around the little island, she tested her leg. Before long she demanded, "Let's get going and see what we can find in that plane."

"We can wait a little longer. You're limping almost as bad as you did that night we went dancing," Joe teased. "I don't think it would be a good idea for us to leave yet."

She looked up at him and smiled. "I'm not hurt that badly," she teased back, before growing somber. "We shouldn't wait any longer! I'm fine. We may have a long way to go, so we better get going now." She started off through the waist deep mud and water, but fell face down when she came to the first small patch of vegetation.

Dragging her back onto dry ground, Joe said, "We'll wait just a little longer. You can't travel yet."

"Sargento, I'm okay. I can make it."

The sound of rifle shots off in the distance ended the discussion. They hurried to investigate. Joe made Louise stay close beside him. He pulled her along helping her to walk. He guessed it was close to 1400 hours when they stopped to take a break. They took time to check their bandages. The watertight patch on her wound seemed to be holding well, as were the ones on his legs.

The sound of small arms fire increased as they drew closer to the hapless plane. She had skidded through the mud and come to rest with one wing in the trees and the other, or what was left of it, buried in the swamp. Her fuselage lay in about two feet of water with gaping holes riddling the body of the plane. Castro's troops had stationed themselves all round the wreck and were pumping rounds into the plane and her crew. The trapped men put up a gallant fight.

Joe and Louise, slipping up as close as they dared, hid, watching the carnage. It made Joe feel sick to his stomach to witness such a massacre and not be able to help. Only one man was left standing. He cursed the soldiers in English and fired his side arm. He took out several of the Cuban soldiers, but he didn't have a chance to survive. They had him outnumbered thirty-to-one. They kept up the assault, firing continuously. As each round hit the lone airman, he would fall down, then get up again to fire. He kept yelling, "Come and get me, you commie imbeciles." He bravely fought until a bullet between his eyes took him down for the last time. Joe and Louise watched helplessly.

Joe knew if they had joined in the battle, they would now be lying in the swamp as dead as those poor fellows. Then where would the mission be? Those men back at the camp were their first responsibility. They had a job to do and getting killed so he could feel brave for a few minutes would not have helped the airman and would circumvent the completion of their mission.

When the NAC was sure that the Americans were no longer able to defend themselves, they moved in. They mutilated the dead men by cutting off body parts. Then they turned and ravaged the plane, stripping her of her guns and cargo. The soldiers shouted in Spanish.

"What are they saying?" Joe asked Louise.

"One of them wants to burn the plane, saying it's no good, but the leader wants to leave it. He wants to salvage some parts later."

"It looks like they are taking everything. They didn't leave anything we could use," Joe whispered, even though they were too far away to be heard. "I don't think we should take a chance on being caught. There's nothing left to salvage. Maybe we should just slip away and leave it."

Louise disagreed. "No way. We'll stay to see if they leave anything behind. They might miss some ammo for the fifty-caliber gun. We sure could use anything they don't take and if they miss some food, we can use that too. I'm hungry, so let's wait. They'll leave soon. That was an Americano crew flying that plane. If they are sending Americanos, they must be going to help us soon. I wonder what's keeping them?"

"It's hard to tell what may have held them up. I knew they wouldn't leave us hanging out on a limb and not give us support." He wanted to give her a little hope, even though he was starting to wonder if they had been left in the lurch. She was right. If the Americans had been coming, they would have been there by now. He wondered if they were on their own with their meager supplies.

After the soldiers left, they went to the plane looking for anything that might have been overlooked by the raiders. They found very little. The NAC had been pretty thorough and had stripped the plane of just about everything.

"Louise, can you get back into that small space there in the tail section? It looks like there might be something there. Do you see that box way back there?" Joe asked, turning to look at her. "It looks like something might have gone through that hole in the tail section. I'll go outside and see if the NAC missed anything there, while you try to retrieve whatever that is in there." Even though he dreaded getting back into the water, he waded back out. He found a bundle, which had been part of the supplies they were to drop to the exiles. He also found a large crate full of paper and about fifteen pounds of black beans and about ten pounds of rice sealed in plastic. Feeling hungry, he chose to take the beans and rice, knowing it would add twenty-five pounds to their packs. He returned to the plane carrying the box of dried food. Louise had also hit the jackpot when she crawled back into the tail section. The NAC had missed ten boxes of C-rations, one hundred and eighty rounds of fifty-caliber ammo and the plane's small first aid kit.

They had taken the bodies of the crewmembers as trophies, to be photographed and used for propaganda. Fresh blood covered the floor and most of the interior of the fuselage.

Joe looked pleased when he saw the ammunition. "Put that first aid kit in your pack, but first, see if there's anything in there to help fight infection. We could use some right away. I would like to take a look at our wounds while it is still daylight. How do you feel?"

"Not to worry, I am fine," she said. "Your legs must be hurting very badly by now."

"Louise, I forgot all about my little scratches when you got hit. Don't worry about me. I think we will spend the night in the plane. I don't think the soldiers will be coming back today and it will get dark before we could reach camp. I don't want to spend the night out there in the swamp. What do you think?"

"That would be best. I know you want to be back at the camp with the guys, but we don't have enough time before dark. It would be best to stay right here."

They found a dry spot free of the doomed airmen's blood and settled in for the night. As they slumped down on the floor of the old plane for a little rest, they soon realized all the excitement had given them an adrenaline high, which made them too wired to sleep. Joe snuggled down beside Louise slipping his arm under her head. A full moon cast a little light inside the wreckage. Joe leaned over and kissed Louise, her lips were soft and supple under his. A surge of desire raced through his body and his kiss became more urgent. He was a man and she was a woman. Joe could not count on tomorrow. All they had was now. "I love you, Louise." Louise returned the kiss and the embrace for a moment, but then she stiffened and gently pulled away.

"I love you, too, but I cannot. My mother told me to keep gift until married. I listen to her. Not cheat my man. Maybe, Sargento, you be my man. Maybe, maybe not, what you think?"

Joe sat up. What was he thinking? Taking advantage of a young girl under his command. He silently berated himself, not saying anything to her.

Louise reached over and took hold of his hand. "Silly girl? You think Louise foolish for keeping herself clean until married?"

"No, Louise. I think you are wonderful. Not all girls are virgins today. I should have realized. I'm a fool. Can you forgive me?" He was used to the type of girl he met in sleazy bars, immoral and willing. Louise squeezed his hand. "You don't like me....now?"

Joe reached down and kissed her tenderly on her parted lips, careful not to brush against her. "I love you even more. Keep your gift until you get married."

He sat up, discreetly moving away from her. "Try to get some sleep. You must be exhausted. I'll keep watch." Fighting off sleep, he sat looking out the large hole in the side of the broken aircraft. Louise had maneuvered closer and now slumbered with her head in his lap. He fought to stay awake, but soon his head began to nod and he dozed off.

Sometime in the early morning hours, he awoke suddenly. His back was still wet, and he was shaking from the cold. Louise was curled up in a ball, still sleeping. Joe found that he had snuggled up against her to keep warm. There was a sudden sound; something or someone was out there. He picked up his carbine and moved slowly and quietly, trying not to wake her. He stumbled over something on the floor of the plane. A split second later, he heard the metallic "click" of a round going into the chamber. Louise had just loaded her carbine.

"Don't shoot. It's me," Joe whispered. "I think I heard something out there."

He went over to the big hole to look out into the darkness. He knew that he had heard something and wished that they had gone back to the camp. Could those soldiers have come back for something? It was unlikely, because they had taken everything. He breathed a sigh of relief when she identified the sound as an alligator bumping against the side of the plane, probably drawn by the smell of blood. He couldn't see it, but he could hear the ugly beast moving around in the water. Undisturbed by the creature, Louise put down her weapon and returned to her fetal position. Joe was too cold to sleep. He had never liked being wet and he hadn't been dry since he landed in the swamp two nights ago.

He longed for the sun to come and warm his bones. Perhaps they could risk a small fire, but there was not one dry thing within a five-mile radius except parts of the plane and they couldn't risk a fire with the fumes from the spilled fuel. He longed to smoke a cigarette, but even if they hadn't been damp, he wouldn't light one in the plane. He sat listening to the silence and thought of home. If he was there now, he would be climbing out of a warm bed to get ready for work. The smell of freshly brewed coffee and ham and eggs would welcome him as he sat eating with the other guys in a cozy restaurant. He realized he had always taken the simple things in life for granted, but now in this strange place, he missed them very much. He felt homesick. He wanted to go home.

It was almost daylight when he felt a slight movement at his side, so quiet he almost didn't hear it.

"Good morning, Sargento," Louise said softly. "Did you sleep?'

"Some, not much. I was too wet and cold to get comfortable. Go back to sleep, you'll need your beauty sleep. We'll head back to camp before long."

"No, Sargento. I can't go back to sleep. I'm hungry and wet. I slept a little, but I was cold. I hurt all over and I need a bath. You want to hear my dream? I dream we got married. What do you think Joe…you think we might?"

"That could happen." Joe whispered in her ear.

"I hope my dream will happen," she said, speaking so low Joe could hardly hear.

He couldn't do anything about the wet, cold conditions or the bath, but he could assuage her hunger. "We'll open one case of C-rations and have something to eat. There are three boxes in each case. We'll share one and start back as soon as it is light enough to see where we are going." Joe looked out at the uninviting terrain. "Why would anyone want to live in a place like this? I would just let them have it and go back to the good old USA."

"It's not all like this," she said. "The rest of Cuba is very pretty. It has green hills, vineyards and lush gardens. It's a good country. It has mountains like in your country and the weather is not always so cold. It's almost always warm here."

"I could use some of that warmth right now. I'm freezing," Joe complained, wiggling his toes in his boots to get some circulation in them.

"It'll be warm soon," she promised, as she snuggled close to him. Their shared body heat helped keep them warm until the sun peeked over the treetops. With it came the wonderful heat of the day.

"I think it's light enough now," Joe said. "Let's have something to eat and hit the trail." Taking a container of Spam from the pack, he used the key fastened to its bottom to twist the top off the can. They found a small package of crackers in wax-coated paper. Louise placed a piece of cloth she had found as a table cloth on the seat of the plane. The crackers were stale and tasted like a candle, but to them it was a banquet.

Sharing that meager meal somehow made them feel close to each other. As hungry as they were, they shared only one package, saving the rest for the others. They knew that they would be just as hungry. He opened another small can, marked fruit. He figured that they could share it, but when she saw that it was sliced peaches, she danced around as if they had found a gold mine. She reminded him of a happy child. She was the bright spot in this whole nightmare. Seeing her excitement, Joe decided he didn't really like peaches all that much. "Take them. I just can't stand those things."

"Oh, thank you, Sargento. They're my very favorite food." She slowly ate the peaches, savoring each delicious bite, sipping the syrup slowly to make it last. He smiled as he watched her eat. While she was busy eating, he opened the other boxes. Both contained sliced peaches. Taking the cans out of the boxes, he saved them for her. He felt a little guilty about keeping them from the others, but all those sweets weren't good for them anyway, he reasoned. He was doing them a favor by taking out all those peaches. He slipped them into his pack.

Looking up at the sky, he said, "It's time. The sun is up and we'd better be getting back to the others before they wonder what happened to us, and send out a search party."

"Yes," Louise said. "I'm much better now and I can travel. If we don't leave soon the NAC might come back. We don't want to be here if they do." Louise said a quick prayer. He soon discovered she was a devout Catholic, praying every morning.

They headed back the way they had come with Louise in the lead. She knew the swamp better than he did. Her pack was lighter than his. He carried the fifty-caliber ammo and part of the food they had found. In his weakened condition, he struggled to keep pace with the heavy load. They had only gone about a quarter of a mile, but it seemed like five hundred miles.

Louise let out a muffled scream and ran back toward Joe, nearly knocking him over in her haste. She looked like she wanted to jump into his arms.

He looked past the frightened girl and his heart began to skip, pounding loudly in his chest. There in the swamp he saw a large 'gator with just the top of its head and eyes showing above the water. The huge tail made ripples in the water as it came swimming by just about ten feet in front of them. Stopping long enough to let the reptile swim out of sight, Joe held her close and kissed her trembling lips. Teasing, he whispered in her ear, "Thank you, Mr. Alligator." Louise playfully slapped him on the shoulder, giggling softly.

They continued their water soaked trek through the mud and ooze. He didn't want to scare her, but he kept an eye out for ripples in the water, wondering how he would get the packs off in time to shoot the critter. Plus, he didn't want to give away their location. He just hoped they would get back to their base camp in one piece.

Wading in the waist deep water and mud, Louise had trouble making headway. She stumbled and did a belly flop into the foul smelling water, her pack holding her down. Joe grabbed her by the hair, pulling her head out of the water so she could breathe. It had taken them about a day to reach the downed plane; now, on the return trip they had more to carry. They had just about reached the end of their endurance and they were looking at most of the day's journey back to the camp. Their progress had been slow and they still had a long hike ahead of them. Louise struggled with the weight of her pack and Joe barely had the strength to carry his load, much less help with hers. As they sloshed through the smelly water, Joe knew Louise wouldn't be able to keep going much longer and neither would he. He hadn't thought she would be able to handle a pack that weighed half as much as she did.

Louise briefly stopped, looking around the swamp to get her bearings. Joe slipped some of her load into his own pack, hoping to lighten it without her knowing.

"I think you need to rest for awhile," Joe said.

"No, Sargento! I can do it. I don't need to stop."

"Well, I do," he snorted. "We won't make it back to the camp today. Let's find a spot where we can rest for awhile. We need it," Joe said, breathing heavily. He was at the point of exhaustion. They crawled out of the water onto a fallen tree trunk, grateful that the limbs of the tree held the trunk out of the water, keeping it dry, but it was too narrow for them to stretch out. Finally, they moved on until they found a small island and collapsed on it. It wasn't much; just a pile of sand, but it was out of the water with enough vegetation to provide some cover. They took off their packs and Joe went looking for something to build a small fire, hoping to keep them warm and to protect them from the swamp critters that roamed the night. Joe leaned over to pick up a stick. He froze, listening. Voices.

"They'll be coming this way. I know Louise will use this path because she knows it best," Gabby said.

Sam agreed, pushing back the vegetation as he walked through the water and muck. "You're right. We'll keep looking for them here."

Now Louise heard the voices, too. "Sargento Joe! Someone is coming down that path we came in on." She paused, listening. "I can't tell who it is, but someone is coming for sure."

"Listen, Louise." Joe strained to hear and then smiled. "It sounds like Gabby." He listened as the voices came closer. "Yes, it is Gabby. Don't call out to him because there might be soldiers nearby."

As they came closer, Louise couldn't contain herself. Happily, she sang out, "Here, we are over here," alerting the men as to their location. Gabby and Sam came running, so happy they'd found their friends and that they were alive.

"Sargento Joe, let me have that pack," Gabby said as soon as he came to their side. "Louise, give yours to Sam and let's get back to camp. We'll get a fire going so you can warm yourselves."

They headed back to the hideout. Learning the plane was from the US, Sam and Gabby were in high spirits and couldn't wait to eat some of the food they had brought back with them.

CHAPTER FOURTEEN

After they got back, Louise stayed so close to Joe that she could have been a shadow, following him at all times. Sometimes, he would have to send her on an errand so he could relieve himself. He wondered if she feared he would leave her or if she thought he could protect her.

"Louise, let's get our own foxhole ready. Those guys will be coming down that road soon and you saw what happened at the plane," Joe said reminding her about the massacre. "We want to be ready to give them a warm reception. We'll be moving around quite a bit, but we will need a place where we can keep an eye on the action and still stay as safe as possible." Choosing a spot alongside of the fifty-caliber gun, they dug in. Joe had never seen red soil before. As they began to dig, some of the men who had finished their own foxholes came to help.

"Sargento! Sargento!" Gabby came running back into camp and said. "There was another airdrop just before we came for you. I sent five people to pick up the supplies. John just got back. He said the supplies landed on a dam some distance away. The NAC got there ahead of them and they shot our men on the spot. John had missed the turn in the road or they would have gotten him, too."

It seemed the NAC were consistently a step ahead of the little band of rebels. They would have to live on what they had hidden prior to the invasion. They had the foresight to hide food, water and weaponry at various locations throughout the swamp. They knew they might have to retreat into the mountains if things went against them, and they were prepared for a long battle. They could not have foreseen the problem with the fifty-caliber ammo being lost in the airdrop, nor did they know that they needed an extra barrel for the gun itself. Joe chalked it up to poor planning on the part of the US Government. He knew that the people who had trained these poor saps should have taught them to change the barrel after so many rounds. The mortar shells being damaged in the drop couldn't have been helped, either. 'Fortunes of War' as they say.

They shouted for joy when they saw another plane had dropped its cargo about a mile away from the camp. Joe sent ten men to pick it up. Expecting food, ammo and some new weapons, they were bitterly disappointed with what they found. A few cartons of C-rations had survived the landing, but the rice, and beans had splashed down in about five feet of swamp water, and were ruined. They also found about a ton of propaganda papers. If a battle could be fought with wet paper and ruined beans and rice, then they would be well armed. They did manage to salvage a little of the black beans and rice, which had been packed in plastic bags.

They also found some old, rusty M-1 rifles, probably Korean War vintage, leftovers from the 38th parallel, Joe thought in disgust. He inspected the weapons. They looked like they hadn't been cleaned since 1951. A man would be putting himself in grave danger just to fire one of these old relics. They set about cleaning and oiling the rifles as best they could. They had to use what they had. It was as simple as that. Joe knew they had to get them in working order. To his surprise the rifles worked well after the men used a little elbow grease. Joe had to take his hat off to Mr. Garand, the fellow who designed these marvelous shooters. They stashed them in a secret place in the swamp in case they needed them later. They also hid all of the extra supplies that they couldn't carry.

Joe sent Louise over to the listening post, where two of the rebels manned the radio. He sent some of the men out on patrol. While they were gone, he went through the rest of the C-rations and found seven or eight more cans of peaches, which he saved for Louise. She had trouble using the little P-38 can opener that came in the rations and would bring her containers to Joe to be opened.

"I don't want to bother you, but will you open this for me?" she would ask.

He never told her, but he found pleasure in doing little things for her and was pleased that she would ask him for help. It was the least he could do for her. He marveled that a young girl would put herself in danger to fight for what she thought was right.

That afternoon, Louise and Joe sat quietly beside each other, each lost in thought while she ate a can of peaches. Looking at him, she asked. "Why did you do it?"

Joe came out of his reverie. "Why did I do what?"

"Why did you fight for me at the club that night?" She slowly finished the last slice of peach, rolling it around in her mouth to savor the last of the fruit.

"You had as much right to be there as anyone, and I didn't like the way that man at the door treated you. Besides, I was quite fond of you even then," he admitted.

His last remark brought a shy smile to her face. She nodded. "Me, too, Sargento Joe."

He thought he would take a chance and ask her the question he had been tempted to ask many times before. "I answered your question, now you answer mine."

Louise frowned and looked puzzled. "What question? I tell you."

"Why did you leave America? I know this is your homeland, but why would you choose to get involved in this covert mission? Surely you understand how much danger you are exposing yourself to by coming here."

Raw pain contorted her lovely features and tears sprang to her eyes. He regretted asking, but once she started to explain through the water works, he just listened.

"They killed my mama. She worked for Batista as a domestic and English interpreter. They caught her on her way home and hanged her. They left her body hanging by the side of the road. They put a sign around her neck saying this will happen to all persons who serve Batista. They told Papa that she run away, but she loved us. I no believe them. They killed her." Louise put her head on her arm and cried softly.

Joe felt like a jerk bringing up old memories and making her cry. Still, he let her talk.

"On April 18, 1958, we put mama in the ground. Castro promised papa that if any of his men hurt her that he would see they were shot."

"Did he punish the men responsible?" Joe asked.

She laughed and spit on the ground. "No!" She rattled off a spate of Spanish before she remembered that he could not understand her. "Three months later, Castro came to see papa. He said he knew who had hurt mama. It was a bandit named Miguel. He would catch and execute him." She stopped and shivered in the hot sun. "Then he knelt by me and promised he would come for me after my Festa-Quinceanera. I would live with him in the big house. His cigar smoke was smelly in my face. It choked me and I was afraid. I didn't want to leave papa and live with him."

"What happened," Joe prodded, waiting until she found her voice again, her eyes reliving the events of the past.

She licked her dry lips and spoke as one watching a movie. "Papa didn't say a word, but as soon as Castro left us, papa say we are going to America."

Joe smoothed the shiny straight hair from her brow and pushed it back in place. "But why did you leave America? Your father took you there to keep you safe."

"Now I know truth. Bristol told me Castro's men killed my mother because she worked for Batista. Castro knows truth. He lied to us. Castro is a bad man. Castro must die. I help."

Joe clenched his fists. Bristol! He should have known he was at the bottom of this. He knew the CIA was orchestrating the overthrow of Castro, but it angered him that Bristol would use a young girl to help them carry out their plan. Poor Louise, he thought as he stroked her long, black hair and pulled her into his arms. Her hatred and desire for vengeance played right into the hands of Bristol.

He held her until she fell asleep. It only took a few minutes because they were both exhausted. It had been three days, four nights since either of them had any real sleep, except for that little catnap at the plane, and that couldn't be called real sleep. The bone chilling cold and stressful conditions kept them from the kind of sleep they both desperately needed. He figured the men were exhausted, but they never complained. They just did as they were told, going about their duties. That was new to him. In the past, the men he worked with on the construction job always griped over the least inconvenience. On the other hand, these fellows had it much rougher, but never complained. His heart went out to them, and his respect for them as men grew as they came and went without a word. Some were injured and most were tired and hungry. Yet, they all seemed to be in good spirits. It boggled the mind. He knew these men were different. He finally came to the conclusion that, like the troops at Valley Forge, men who are striving to gain their independence from tyranny are willing to go that extra mile.

They took orders from a stranger, they seemed eager to please and he believed they would put their life on the line for him. That was a humbling thought. He seemed to have their complete trust, though he hadn't done anything to earn it. Maybe just being there was reason enough.

Joe liked the fact that these hardened combat infantry soldiers had taken Louise under their wing and treated her like a younger sister, although many of them were about her age. If they noticed she was the only one eating peaches, they never said a word. He secretly thought they were glad for her. The Cuban exiles were respectful and protective of her.

After she woke up, Joe and Louise hunkered down at a point where they could get a bird's eye view of the road. During the night, not a single vehicle appeared, but now it looked like downtown Columbus at rush hour. Anything that was able to move came chugging down that dirt road. Old cars, with their radiators steaming and their horns honking, crowded the byway. The locals were running, hoping to escape the fighting. The civilians posed no threat, but the military units that would be coming close behind them were legal military targets.

The little unit of ill-equipped guerrillas had orders to stay hidden from the locals as much as possible, and not to attack until the friendly troops and their helicopters were gone.

Louise said, "Sargento, can we stop one of them and ask them what is happening down the road?"

"I don't think so. You might as well let the whole world know that we are here."

"I can do it. I would blend in. They won't suspect me."

At first, Joe disagreed. "No, it's too dangerous." However, he knew she was right. He was hungry for information. He finally agreed, after cautioning her to be careful. "Okay, Louise. You can do it, but I want men on both sides of the road just in case they get wise to you." Turning to Gabby, Joe said, "Keep her covered. If you see anyone making a wrong move, let him have it with everything you've got. Remember that Louise will be out in the open. Don't hit her."

Louise quickly went behind a bush and changed from her combat fatigues into a tattered and dirty outfit, that blended in with the other refugees. She walked out near the side of the muddy road and waved to passers by. Finally, an old pickup truck loaded with worn out furniture stopped beside her. Several children looked down at her from among the beds and tables loaded on the back of the truck. There were arms and legs everywhere. It put Joe in mind of Ma Kettle and her brood. A portly woman sat on the passenger's side and a thin, wrinkled man drove.

"What are you doing out here all alone? Get on the back of the truck. You can ride with us. You need to get away. Many soldiers are coming up the road behind us. If you stay here, they will get you," the man said kindly.

"Thank you, but I am waiting for my brother. He should be along at any moment," she lied.

The little gray-headed fellow shook his head sadly, and with a grinding of gears, he coaxed the old truck into motion. The heavyset lady didn't like leaving her behind. "Make her come with us. We can't leave her here."

The poor harried little man stopped again and came back to where Louise was standing. "You'd better come with us. Your brother may not get through all this traffic and I don't want to leave you here alone with those soldiers. They can be mucho bad." The little man shook his head.

Louise shook her head and waved him on. The Catholic lady made the sign of the cross as the old truck sputtered away with a jerk, leaving a cloud of blue oil smoke trailing behind it. They were scared and running for their lives, carrying all their worldly possessions with them.

As they watched the little truck drive out of sight, Joe had an idea. If he could get Louise to go with the refugees, it might save her from being captured or killed. She would have to think that she was doing a great service for her sergeant; otherwise, she wouldn't go. Grabbing a pair of binoculars from Gabby, Joe began to sweep the countryside. If he could find some escapees who looked like they needed help, he would order Louise to guide them to safety. The Cuban soldiers were going to show up soon and she would be out of harm's way when the fighting started.

Searching frantically, he finally spotted a family stumbling along as they carried bundles of charcoal out of the swamp. They appeared to be a middle-aged man and woman with a young lad of nine or ten. They were dressed in rags and had no shoes. The man wore a shirt with no sleeves and the woman wore a tattered old dress that once might have been yellow. They were loaded down with sacks of charcoal. The boy staggered under a sack far too heavy for him. Struggling, he fell to his knees into the water, careful to not let his burden get wet. His father yelled at the lad, hitting him about the head with a short piece of rope that he had used to tie his bundles. Crying great tears, the child managed to stand on his feet. He ran to keep up with his parents.

"Look at that!" Joe said through clenched teeth. "I think I'll give that man a good beating," he told Louise when she came back to stand beside him.

"Yes, I see them," she said softly, "We can be angry with his father, but we are not in a position like he is. They must meet a quota or face prison or something worse. Fidel Castro always gets his money's worth, no matter what it costs others."

Joe heard the bitterness in her voice. He wanted desperately to help the child, but there was little he could do. Hopefully, if they were successful in their mission, life would improve for all of these people. This might be what he needed to get Louise to a safe place. Joe glanced over at her. "Did you ever have to work like that?"

"Yes, but not in the charcoal; I worked in the sugar cane fields. That was not quite as bad as this," she said.

"I wish I could help those poor folks," he said, watching them stumble down the dirt road. "Maybe you could go with them for awhile, to get them to safety. You can come back as soon as they are in the clear. What do you think?" He held his breath.

"I think you are trying to get rid of me," she said angrily. "I'm not going away. That is final."

Reaching over, he stroked her soft cheek with his finger. "I am only concerned about your welfare."

She looked up at him and batted her eyelashes. "You sure you not trying to send me away?"

Every time he looked into those pretty ebony eyes, his heart melted. The temptation was more than he could resist. Even though he knew this was not the time or the place, he wanted to hold her close and to kiss her. She sensed that he wanted her and she walked eagerly into his arms. Just as their lips met, the first shell hit. It landed about twenty-five yards behind the family in the swamp. Water and smoke splattered the people like a dirty shower. The man and woman dropped their load and ran for cover, but the child just stood there paralyzed with fright.

He was afraid to drop his bundle and didn't know what to do. The first to recover from the initial shock was Gabby. He went running through the mire, picked up the boy on the run and headed for cover.

Joe gave Louise a shove and she sprawled on the ground. "In coming! Get your head down," he yelled at his men. Artillery shells were bursting all around them now, the sound deafening. Mud and smoke filled the air.

"Louise, get over to that foxhole with the radio and see if you can hear anything," he yelled above the thunderous noise of exploding shells. Then the unseen gunner increased his rate of fire and the shells started to fall in earnest. The spotters had called in a fire command and the artillery had their range. Using the scope on his rifle, Joe began a sweep of the trees on the hillside. He knew there would have to be someone coordinating the fire. He located the spotter on the backside of the hill, high up in a tall tree. He caught the glint from his rifle's scope and some leaves that didn't belong on that kind of tree.

"Ben, can you see him? He's up there in that tree with the wilted leaves. I saw the sun reflect off his scope lens a moment ago. Take the binoculars with you and watch for any snipers that may be hidden out there. You'd better take a man with you. Put that guy out of commission or we've all had it. What do you think? Can that mortar reach him from here?" Joe asked Tony.

"No, Sir. We only have the 60-MM and it doesn't have the range to get that far, but we can move it a little closer."

"No, I need you to cover the road. We'll let Ben have a shot at him first. Ben, whatever you do, don't let him get away. You'll need to get off a good clean shot. Try to get him with the first round. We're all counting on you."

"I will take him out before he knows what hit him," Ben grinned. "Trust me."

"Good man," Joe said. "He's all yours." He wanted to move to a safer place, but they had no safer place. The swamp encircled them and they occupied the only dry ground for miles.

The shelling increased, causing the number of casualties to mount. The radio foxhole took the first hit, the one Joe had ordered Louise to man. Fear clutched at him as he ran toward the foxhole on wounded legs, fighting hard to hold back the tears. Reaching the pit, he looked down in, gagging. Smoke poured from the crater made by the 105 MM H E (high explosive round) and chunks of flesh and dismembered limbs were strewn about the hole. It reminded him of a deer he had seen on the Interstate highway when an eighteen-wheeler had run over it. There was nothing in that hole that one could recognize as human. It looked as if someone had poured the scraps from a butcher's shop into it. Joe stood beside the carnage and vomited.

A second later Gabby joined him by the pit. "Who?" he asked soberly.

"Louise," Joe answered.

Gabby didn't say a word. He just crossed himself and began to pray.

Joe fell down to the ground with great, heart-wrenching sobs that shook his entire body. He felt grief like he had never experienced before. He cried for the beautiful young girl and for all they might have had together. He blamed himself for her death because he had ordered her to man the radio. He would have given his life for her but now it was too late. How he hated this mission. Where were his reinforcements? Where were the Americans? He felt rage boiling inside of him and he grabbed his gun. He wanted to pay back whoever had done this to Louise. He wanted to kill. He had never killed another human being, but he wanted to slaughter the soldiers. He wanted to destroy them all. He pushed his sleeve across his eyes to wipe away the tears and started to rise when he felt a hand on his shoulder.

When he looked up, he saw Louise crying silently, the tears running down her face. She blessed herself with the sign of the cross. Jumping up, Joe wrapped his arms around her and hugged her with all his might. He held on so tightly that she could barely breathe. He felt he had been given a second chance. He could hardly believe she was still alive. His emotions, which had plummeted to the lowest depths, now soared to the heavens. "Louise, I thought you were in that hole. I thought you were dead. Where were you?"

A bit embarrassed, she admitted, "I had to go to the bathroom. I went into the woods."

"Who did we lose?" he asked.

"Two men. Roberto and Mureo were in this hole," she said as she looked down at the dismembered bodies. She began to pray in Spanish.

"It sure don't look like them anymore. It don't look like anybody," she said softly.

"Have we lost anyone else?" Joe asked.

She gave no reply. She stood transfixed, peering into the smoking foxhole.

"Have we lost anyone else?" he repeated.

When she still did not answer, Joe shook her yelling, "Did we lose anyone else?"

"Just these two men, I think," she stammered. There was a short pause in the shelling, and in the distance they heard the crack of a single gunshot.

"That sounds like Ben's rifle," Gabby said. "He likes his old bolt action 30-06 for serious shooting. Maybe now the shelling will stop."

When Ben and his amigo came back into camp, everyone cheered loudly and slapped them on the back.

"Good job," Joe said, as he shook hands. "I knew we could depend on you."

They had succeeded in their mission. The shelling continued, but without the spotter whom Ben and his amigo had taken out, the big guns were shooting blind. Even so, they managed to score another hit. Another man was shot in the stomach as he leaned against a tree. The concussion of the shell burst sent him about twenty feet into the air. He came crashing back to the ground with blood running out of his mouth and ears. The man struggled for each painful breath, crying out for water. When they tried to give him some, he choked on the liquid. He died an agonizing hour later.

Everyone sat in total silence for quite sometime. The smell of death permeated the air around them. Joe figured the men were thinking about their own mortality. As suddenly as it had started, the shelling stopped. Most of the men were praying the rosary; just about all of them had one. Not being a Catholic himself or having a religious background, Joe didn't understand what they were doing. He thought it had religious significance, so he waited before he called a conference. Finally, he called the men together.

"Let's bury these poor fellows," he ordered matter-of-factly. "Make sure there is no identification on any of the bodies so their families won't suffer if we lose this battle." He had to shout to make his voice heard above the exploding shells. "Put all the men in the radio foxhole and cover it up."

"It is a terrible thing to be buried in such a lonely place as this, with no one to mourn, or to put flowers on the grave," Louise whispered. "I would not wish it on anyone. When I die, I want to be buried on a hill where the sun shines all the time and the earth is dry and warm."

Joe wished she would stop talking like that. He had almost lost her once and he didn't want to think about living without her. He changed the subject. "Come with me," Joe said to his band of rebels. "Let's see how much damage has been done. I think it's about time we did a little damage of our own."

She followed obediently, without comment. The men silently began to assess the damage. Sam climbed high up a tree and signaled that some military vehicles were coming down the road.

"Okay," Joe said. "It's our turn. Let's see if that little mortar can hit the road now. Get ready. We'll hit them as they come around the curve." Joe wanted to know what they were up against, so he told Louise to talk to Sam. She spat out Spanish and asked Sam how many trucks and military vehicles he saw and what kind they were. Were there any tanks or APC's (armored personal carriers)?

After talking to Sam for a while, Louise reported, "No tanks, but three big trucks and two jeeps."

"Okay. They want a fight. Let's give'm one." Joe functioned on pure adrenaline. "Any of them that we can take out now will be a few less for the US forces to deal with when they get here." The trucks were coming back from the fighting. They were heading to the rear area to get supplies and reload. In a short time, they would be back in the fight. "We need to get them with the first volley," Joe said. "We may be outnumbered, but the element of surprise will work in our favor. Hit them fast and hard. The mortar will stop the lead truck. You men with rifles get as many of them as you can. Don't let any of them escape into the swamp. Whatever you do, don't miss when you fire. Keep dropping mortar rounds in on them to keep them confused, and remember, shoot to kill."

"Louise, direct the men to get that fifty-caliber over there where it can do the most good and remind them, short bursts. We only have 1,000 rounds, so make every shot count."

"The convoy is moving very slow, Sargento," Louise reported, after speaking to Sam. "They are towing one of the trucks."

"Good! That will slow them down and give us a better shot at them," he said. "Please don't miss. Wait and think. Don't fire the fifty unless you're sure of your target, and whatever you do, keep undercover. We've lost too many and I don't want to lose another man or woman," he added, looking directly at Louise. "Save all the ammo you can. Try not to waste any shells. We will need it later." He paused. "You know I think I have an idea that just might work."

The little band of exiles looked expectantly at him. "Louise, if you are willing, I want you to act as a decoy."

"What do you want me to do?"

"Put on that skirt and blouse and take your hair out of that ponytail. Let it hang loose and brush it so that it shines. Then stand over by that big tree and look pretty. When they see you, they will either slow down or stop. Wave and smile at them. Try to distract them long enough for our men to zero in on them. Then jump into that foxhole and don't stick your head out until all of the shooting is over. Do you understand? Can you do it?"

"I can," she said, hurrying behind a thicket to change clothes and undo her hair. In a few minutes she reappeared, looking more like a girl ready to go on a date than what she was, a girl caught up in a dangerous situation, her life, as theirs, hanging in the balance.

"Remember, the minute the firing starts get into that foxhole," Joe ordered. "Don't be foolish and don't take any chances. I don't want any dead heroes. That goes for all of you," he told the men.

Everyone took their places as soon as they heard the convoy coming down the road. The trap was set. Louise stood by the big tree waving to the soldiers in the first jeep. They slowed down, waving back to her. "Hey, baby. Want to go for a ride?" the one in the front passenger's side yelled. They all hooted and laughed.

In an instant, the first mortar round hit the lead truck. It went right through the windshield and hit the fuel tank located behind the seat. The men in the cab never saw it coming. Two other bombs walked down the length of the truck, killing everyone inside it. The fifty opened up on the first jeep, taking it out of action. The soldiers jumped out, running for the woods, but they were killed before they could reach cover. The first large truck rear-ended the disabled jeep, causing it to come to an abrupt stop. The crew scrambled out, trying to run, but quickly raised their hands in surrender when they realized that they were caught with their defenses down. The last truck, the one in tow, was unoccupied, but was pulling a large trailer. The second jeep turned as if to escape, but was hit by a mortar round.

Joe couldn't believe the outcome. The guerrillas had the upper hand and the Cuban soldiers didn't have a leg to stand on. They were all down except for the handful that surrendered after the first shots were fired. Some of Joe's men wanted to execute the soldiers, but others thought that killing them would make the rebels as bad as the soldiers. Only seven of the Cuban soldiers were alive. The battle had ended without the enemy firing a single shot.

"That seemed too easy," Joe worried aloud. "Go search that last truck and see what's inside. Be careful."

Gabby and Sam cautiously crept toward the trailer. They recoiled in horror when they opened the doors. The stench of dead and decaying bodies rushed out and hit them, along with the odor of feces and urine. They quickly put a handkerchief over their nose and mouth.

Upon closer inspection, they could see that not all of the people in the truck were dead. A few of them barely clung to life. The live ones stumbled, falling out of the truck onto the road, blinking in the bright sunlight. The men rushed to help these pitiful pieces of humanity, dragging them away from the area to a shaded spot near the tree line. They had been crowded inside the truck with their hands tied behind their backs and couldn't remove their trousers to relieve themselves. They had been packed in like sardines and were so crowded they had to climb atop the dead bodies in order to breathe. After about three days in the truck without food or water, they had given up hope.

The trucks were brand new GMCs, gifts to Fidel Castro from the good people of the United States. They were refrigeration trucks, given in good faith to be used to haul fresh fruit to market. The refrigeration was not turned on. That made them hot boxes with little or no fresh air.

Joe learned the men were prisoners from the fighting on the beaches. They were part of the 2506th Brigade. The survivors were dehydrated and weak. More then half of the captives had died. Sixteen of them were alive, but only twelve were strong enough to walk. They did not have time to bury the dead, so they pushed the vehicles into the swamp. Hiding them from Castro's air search was essential. They had to bury the evidence. Moving the trailer down next to the swamp, they placed all the dead bodies into it. Then using the only truck that was still operating, they pushed the trailer into the deep hole. It slowly sank into the murky water, but refused to submerge completely. One of the men waded out into the muddy water to open the back door of the trailer. The water rushed into the box and it sank deep enough to cover the entire trailer. Next, they drove the remaining truck into the swamp. It settled down into the ooze and disappeared from view. For a few minutes, bubbles came to the surface until the engine died. That spot became a mass watery grave for the freedom fighters. The men bowed their heads, Louise said a few words, and they all solemnly made the sign of the cross.

A shout came from the mortar position. The men, who had been manning the 60, ran for cover.

"What's going on?" Joe asked Louise, who was ducked behind a bush, changing into her jungle uniform.

"I don't know," she said, trying to hurry.

"You had better come with me to see what the problem is," he said, hurrying toward the men with Louise running to keep pace. As they approached the gun emplacement, one of the men said excitedly, "She is going to blow up. The propellant didn't ignite on the last round and the round...she is stuck in the tube." The men hid behind trees.

"There are two ways to handle a thing like this." Joe walked over to the gun. "One way is to give the tube a good kick." Everyone ducked when he kicked it. "That method usually dislodges the round and it drops down the tube and is fired. In this case, it didn't work, so now we go to plan 'B'. Joe held his breath, carefully picked up the mortar tube, and carried it gingerly to the deepest hole available.

"Louise, ask one of the men to come and help me."

"No, Sargento. I'll do it. What do you want me do?"

"Louise, this is no time to argue with me. Now send one of the men over here so we can get that thing out of the tube," Joe commanded.

"The men are afraid and don't want to help."

"Well, all right. They have good reason to be afraid," he said. "I'm going to get down into this hole. Take the tube and hold it level. When I give you the word, tilt it down. I will try to catch the bomb as it comes out of the tube. I want you to know that if I miss it, we both die."

"You not miss, Sargento. I trust you."

Holding his hands cupped over the end of the tube, she tilted it slightly when he gave the order and the round slid slowly out of the end of the gun tube. Joe latched onto it with his shaking hands, letting the detonator slip in between his fingers. He carefully carried the bomb to the far end of the pit, placed it gently onto the floor of the foxhole and very gently covered it with about two feet of loose dirt. He would have liked to detonate it, but didn't want to make any more noise. Ben and Gabby came out from hiding and finished filling the hole.

"You are very brave, my Sargento," Louise said admiringly.

Joe didn't answer her. He lay down on the ground shaking like a leaf. She thought him brave, but it took every ounce of resolve to grab that bomb. He had acted out of desperation.

CHAPTER FIFTEEN

The sixteen survivors were asked to join the little band of freedom fighters, but they declined. They were too weak and sick causing them to be afraid. Joe learned that the prisoners had been on their way to a firing squad in Havana. They were to be shot before the newsreel cameras, without a trial, to show the world what happens to those who rebel against the glorious Peoples Republic of Cuba.

Joe was in a dilemma. They had seven prisoners and nowhere to secure them. He felt uncertain about the sixteen survivors. If caught, they might be scared enough to turn the exiles in to Castro to save their own hides. He wondered whom he could trust. He had two options, trust the survivors or kill them. He chose to trust them. On the other hand, he knew he couldn't trust the prisoners. Some of the survivors wanted to shoot the prisoners, but Joe refused. "No, that would make us as bad as they are." Joe knew that the prisoners would turn them into Castro's crowd in a heartbeat, if given half a chance. Not wanting to find himself and his men in front of a firing squad, he was ready to make a decision. He and his group had a job to do. He talked to the survivors.

"Where will you go, and how will you get back home?" Joe asked.

One of the men stepped forward and said, "We have families living near here. We'll stay with them until we find a boat to take us back to our own towns." Louise translated for Joe.

"Louise, ask them if they will take the prisoners back into the mountains and keep them there for three or four days. Tell them not to shoot them unless they try to get away. Tell them to explain to the prisoners that if one of them makes a break for it, they will all be shot. We have a job to do. We don't have time to care for the survivors who are too weak to fight or the prisoners. Do you think you can find enough food and water to last you for a few days?" Louise interpreted.

"I'm sorry that we don't have enough extras to give you, but we did salvage a little from the convoy. My men took out anything usable before we sank the vehicles. See if there is anything you can use from those trucks."

They found a few pounds of rice and black beans and about twenty gallons of water in five-gallon cans.

Don said, "It'll only be enough for two or three days. We won't feed the prisoners, but we'll give them water. We have some friends who may help us, if they are not too afraid."

"Be careful and don't talk to strangers," Joe said. "I wish you well, my friend. Vaya con Dios." Joe pulled Don to one side and indicated with hand motions that he wanted him to take Louise with them and care for her. "If I hear that she was mistreated, I will hold you responsible. I will come and cut your throat," he said, drawing his finger across his own neck for dramatic effect. It was an empty threat and both men knew it. Joe would never see the men again.

"Louise, come here for a moment," Joe said.

She was trying to get information from the prisoners, but came on the run when he called her. She seemed happy he needed her. Joe worked to control his emotions. The thought that he might never see her again tore at his heart. His main objective though was to save her life.

He put his hand into his pocket and his fingers closed around the little package from the Base Exchange. It was the onyx ring. He'd taken it from his billfold and shoved it in his pocket for safe-keeping. Taking it from its hiding place, Joe said, "Louise, may I have your hand for a moment?"

She placed her small hand in his and he slipped the ring on her finger. It was much too big for her, but she didn't seem to notice or care. Her eyes opened wide. She fingered the ring tenderly. "It is beautiful."

"I want to give you something to remember me by." He smiled. "Besides, it matches your eyes."

"I won't ever forget you, Sargento," she replied, but with a question in her eyes. "A ring…! Is the most beautiful thing that I have ever seen! I love it."

"It's nothing," he said. "Just a trinket."

She held out her hand and admired the ring like it was the Crown Jewels. She squinted her lovely eyes and looked at him suspiciously. "Why would I need something to remember you?" The smile on her face faded to a frown and her happy expression to one of anger and disbelief. "What are you up to?" she hissed, her lower lip protruding into a pout.

"Louise, you're going with Don and his people. We may not be able to avoid capture and I need to know that you're safe." He knew she would throw caution to the wind to stay with him. So, he tried to give her an order. "I need you to go with them to see that they don't shoot the prisoners or turn us in. Can you do that, soldier?"

"No, Sargento. My job is here with you! You need me to interpret for you. The men will not understand you. I stay!"

That took Joe by surprise. She had disagreed with him in the past, but this was the first time she had refused a direct order. "Louise, that is an order! You'll have to obey! Now be a good soldier and help these men find their way out of here."

"No! I not go Sargento! They know how to go home. You just want me to go away. Please do not make me go with them."

"Don, have some of the men drag her if you have to, but get her out of here," Joe commanded. He motioned for them to take her.

Two of the men grabbed her by the arms and started walking toward the hill country. She kicked, screamed and fought them every step of the way. She begged as they forcibly pulled her along the trail. "Please, Sargento, don't make me go. I want to stay with you and do my job."

Joe turned away from her pleading and started to clean his rifle. He knew she would hate him, but he wanted to save her life at any cost. He hid his face from her because she might see the impact that her leaving had on him. He wanted her to get angry, angry enough to leave.

They had only gone about fifty yards when she pulled away from the men and made good her escape. Louise ran back toward the camp. The men came running after her and once again started dragging her away. She cried and pleaded, half in English and half in Spanish.

He turned away and ignored her. She scratched and clawed at them. The poor men simply let her go after about five hundred yards. This time she didn't run in the direction of the encampment, but walked briskly with her head held high, in a sort of triumphal march.

Joe walked to a clearing on the hillside and sat down on a large log. It was decayed and falling apart from the damp climate and the smell of rotten wood filled his nostrils, but he was becoming accustomed to the odor of mildew and stagnant water. He never thought he would miss the odor of that strong perfume that Louise consistently wore, but he did. She had been gone a half-hour and already it seemed like a lifetime. He missed her so much. He seldom felt sorry for himself, but this seemed like the appropriate time. Lighting a cigarette from his last pack, he drew in the smoke then blew it out slowly.

He figured he had cut his own throat because he couldn't communicate with the men without her. Still, she would be safe and that was all that mattered to him. She was gone now and he could forget her. Who was he kidding? He laughed out loud. He could never forget that twinkle in her dark eyes, or the way her long hair glistened when she tossed her head and that scent that she used so freely. He could almost imagine that he could smell it now. Was it only his wishful thinking, or...?

She crept up behind him and sat on the ground a few feet from him. "Hi. My name is Louise and I'm staying. Any objections?" Her black eyes peered at him from beneath half-closed eyelashes.

"Why did you come back?"

"This is my country. I fight for what is right. They killed my mother. I will not turn and run. Louise is a good soldier."

"You know we might get captured."

"Maybe, yes. Maybe, no...I don't know." She scooted closer and laid her head on his knee.

"If they capture us, you know they will probably kill us," he said coldly. "Why are you willing to take such a chance?"

"I could not leave you," she said simply. "Someone has to look after you. It's for sure you can't take care of yourself. Besides," she added softly, "you have no chance without me."

Joe knew she had a point. Without an interpreter, he couldn't lead the exiles. Still, he knew the only chance he had of leaving this place alive was based squarely on a win and they hadn't even come close. The mission was a flop. The landing they had waited for never took place and the promised troops had never come.

"We're not going to get any support from the United States," he said. "We don't have a snowball's chance and there's no changing that fact."

"They will come," she said hopefully.

Joe shook his head. "They're not coming. I don't know why. But I know they would have been here by now."

Louise grew silent, considering the possibility. "Let's go into the mountains," she said. "We're guerrillas and we know that kind of fighting better then this."

"It won't change anything," Joe answered. "We would just become fugitives and wind up with a price on our heads. We'd be outlaws, always on the run, always looking over our shoulder. What kind of life would that be for us? Every peon in a fifteen-mile radius would want to turn us over for the reward. I don't think either of us wants to live like that. Louise, we have no chance of wining this war and you know it. You're a smart girl." Joe squeezed her hand. "You have to go now. Save yourself," he pleaded. "There is nothing you can do to help me. If you stay, you'll be killed. I'm going to order all the men to disperse into small groups and find their way out of here. They may have friends or family who will help them to escape, but I couldn't get out of Cuba if I had ten thousand dollars in my pocket. I'm a blond American. What chance do I have?"

"I don't care. I stay with you. If I stay, the men will stay." She said with resolve. "Why you not want me, Sargento? I would do anything for you. Why are you trying to get rid of me?"

For the first time since her return, he looked at her small, tear-stained face. She had won, but at what cost?

"Louise, it's not that I don't want you. It's just that the thought of you being captured scares me, especially after I saw what they did to the prisoners we helped. What do you think they would do to you? I just couldn't stand to see you hurt," Joe said.

"My job is here, with you…you are my man, I stay with my man!" She began to cry.

Joe pulled her into his arms and held her. For a moment, he imagined they were in America. He would ask her to marry him, take her home to meet his folks, then they would have children and grow old together. That's the way it was supposed to happen. He thought it still might someday if he could keep them both alive. He had never imagined falling in love in a war torn country or perhaps dying at the age of twenty-two. Louise had a brave heart and more guts than some of the men. He gave her a big hug and used his hand to wipe away her tears. In response she snuggled up to him, then unwound his arms and playfully pushed him off the end of the log. He fell on his butt in the mud.

Amid their playful banter, an enormous snake slithered out from under the log and coiled up behind Louise. Joe was the first to see the serpent. He quickly reached out and grabbed Louise's hand. Thinking he was playing with her, she laughed and pulled her hand free. He lunged at her and grabbed her wrist. He forcibly dragged her out of harm's way.

"Come on, Louise. There's a huge snake!" Joe yelled excitedly. He ran away and expected her to follow.

She seemed to think it was funny. She started laughing and chasing the snake. The snake tried to get away. She grabbed hold of its tail and pulled it out into the clearing. Then, catching hold of the reptile's head with both hands, she yelled, taunting Joe, "Come, and see our fine meal. Why are you afraid of your supper? Come back, Sargento. Don't be scared of such a little snake like this one. He will make a fine supper. We roast and eat. Snake very good to eat."

Joe stayed his distance. He had such a great fear of snakes, that even the little ones would send him packing, but this thing was a monster. Its head was nearly as big as a man's head and it looked as round as a man's thigh. He couldn't really tell how long it was because it was all coiled up, but he wanted to put as much distance between that hideous thing and himself as possible. However, looking back he could see that Louise had more supper than she could handle. The snake had decided that it didn't like the idea of being anyone's meal. It began to get a bit annoyed and wanted to go back to its hiding place. Louise had a firm grip on her prize and wasn't about to let go. The slithery creature slowly wrapped itself around her body. The huge reptile began to squeeze the breath out of her. If she wanted to play rough, it could be just as determined as she could. It was a toss up as to who was going to eat whom. Louise was almost covered by the snake's coils and her laughter had turned to moans for help. It had her choked to the point she didn't have enough breath to cry out.

Terrified, Joe ran back to help even though he knew he was fast becoming short of clean underwear! Fear contorted his face and beads of sweat stood out on his forehead, but snake or no snake, he wasn't going to let anything happen to her if he could help it.

One of the men came running to see what all the excitement was about. He said to Joe in a teasing manner, "That snake is more afraid of you, than you are of it."

If that is true, Joe thought, this is one mighty scared reptile, and that snake's knees would be knocking together!! … If a snake had knees that is. He felt his own knees knocking together; in fact, he was shaking all over. He grabbed hold of the snake's head and began to shake uncontrollably. He pulled with all his might to get the snake off of her. Finally, he called out, "Don't just stand there, help me get this thing off of her." The men tried to help, but the snake had entwined her small body so completely they couldn't hit the reptile without hitting her. Three men, and they were no match for the hideous thing.

Joe once read that a constrictor's bite isn't poisonous, but it can be very painful, especially one as big as this. The commentator had explained it would be like getting bit by a pit bull terrier and this fellow had a mouth the size of a Doberman's. Its fangs were nearly two inches long. It could cause a lot of damage if it bit her. Joe didn't have the strength to uncoil that thing from her and her body was going limp. He knew he had a very short time if he was to save her.

"Gabby! Sam! Help!" Joe shouted.

They came running and helped him pull the snake's head away from Louise while Gabby chopped off the snake's head with his machete. Gabby had insisted on keeping one with him most of the time and Joe was glad that he had. Gabby had to chop and saw at the head several times before he dismembered it. Blood squirted everywhere. It ran down Joe's hands and arms and splattered on his shirt. After what seemed like hours, the snake finally relinquished its hold on her, its coils relaxing as it died. Joe carried Louise several feet from the dead snake. He sat down on the ground holding her head in his lap until her breathing returned to normal. Soon she was up and walking around.

"How are you feeling?" he asked. "Are you okay?"

"Yes, I am fine."

"What was the idea of pulling a stunt like that?" he shouted, angry now that he knew she was okay. "You must be nuts to do a crazy thing like that. You nearly scared me to death. You know how much I hate those things and how afraid I am of them, so what was the big idea?" Angrily stomping off, he found a little puddle of water and began to wash the snake's blood from his hands and shirt. He wondered if all these people were crazy. What had he gotten himself into? His rubbery legs were hardly able to support him. Not wanting the others to see him in such a state, he stumbled off into the woods. His hands were shaking so badly he could hardly hold onto his rifle. He found a secluded spot, just a little clearing, but it would afford him a few minutes of privacy. After checking to make sure there were no snakes or other unpleasant varmints, he slumped down, and after about three tries with shaking hands, he managed to light another cigarette. That incident scared him more then the fall from the plane. He couldn't say jump because he had been unceremoniously pushed out of the plane.

Again, Louise determined not to let him out of her sight, found his hiding place and dropped in for a visit. "Sargento, you not looking so good. Did that mean old snake bite you? Are you sick?" she asked, smiling.

"Yes, I'm sick. Sick of this stinking jungle and everything in it."

Her happy smile turned to a look of deep hurt and she was working hard trying to hold back the tears that had sprung up in her eyes. "Maybe you're sick of me, too," she said, biting her lower lip.

"I'm not sick of you. It's just that I was so afraid for you and you know I have a terrible fear of snakes. I can't even look at them in a pet store," he confessed.

He didn't want to look like a coward and he knew he must look like a wimp to her and the men. How could he look them in the eye, let alone lead them?

She gave him a wide smile, and placed her small hand on his cheek, saying softly, "It's okay. Everyone's afraid of something. Yours is snakes and mine is…. well."

"What is it? What is your greatest fear, Louise?"

"Chocolate chip cookies," she said soberly, her dark eyes twinkling. "When I was a child, a cookie chased me all over the neighborhood and it would have caught me if my little brother hadn't eaten it." She laughed until her sides hurt. Joe failed to see any humor in it.

"Did that cookie give you a good spanking like I'm going to do?" Joe asked with a mischievous grin. He leaned his carbine against a tree and started to walk toward her.

"You wouldn't…would you?" After taking a close look at Joe's expression, she came to the conclusion that her behind just might be a little more comfortable in another location and proceeded to find some pressing business elsewhere.

She started to run as fast as she could, pausing to glance over her shoulder to giggle, knowing full well he couldn't catch her because of his injured legs. They ran into Gabby and Sam in the clearing. Joe could tell that they were up to something. Each of them smiled nonchalantly. Suddenly, Sam took off running across the clearing. He limped and waved his hands in the air, with Gabby in hot pursuit, carrying a large piece of twisted vine that, with a great stretch of imagination, might look like a snake. They laughed, Louise joining them in making sport of the Sargento.

"It wasn't all that funny," he said fuming. "I don't see anything to laugh about."

He tried not to smile, but his reserve broke down and he started to laugh with them. He could imagine that he did look funny running from the viper. The hilarity was a welcome change. "To tell the truth, I was just about scared to death," he admitted.

"If I had been by myself, that thing would have suffocated me," Louise said. She sobered for a moment, but then smiled. "Not to worry. Snake dead now and will soon be dinner for us." She seemed proud of herself for catching such a prize. For six days they had subsisted on meager rations and the big anaconda would provide some much-needed protein.

Some of the men picked up the snake and carried it off. Three of them toted it on their shoulders and about three feet of its tail dragged on the ground behind them. They built a small fire, skinned the critter, then cut it into chunks. They impaled the pieces on green sticks for cooking. The smell of roasting meat, rice and black beans simmering over the open fire drifted into the woods when Joe and Louise walked back to retrieve his carbine.

"It's just like the smell of someone cooking out on a grill at home," Joe said.

"They have some spices. It'll be good. You'll see," she said happily, her voice filled with pride.

Joe didn't want to tell her, but he didn't think he could touch the meat, let alone eat it. The very thought of touching that snake repulsed him. Put it into his mouth? He didn't think so! He could see that these people knew how to survive in the swamps.

While the snake cooked over the open fire, the men teased Joe about being afraid of his supper. With wide grins, one at a time they paraded in front of Joe making eating motions before running away. Joe tried to look angry, but just couldn't pull it off. He enjoyed the ribbing as much as they enjoyed teasing him. The jovial moment came to an abrupt end when a sniper's bullet sent everyone running for cover. Joe calculated the sniper to be about three hundred yards away, stationed across an expanse of water. The water created a barrier that made it hard to get to him. Joe watched Louise go from group to group, passing out orders. Every time she dashed from cover, Joe knew she took a chance of being hit by sniper fire. So far, the gunman hadn't had much luck in hitting anyone, but it was just a matter of time before he might get in a lucky shot. They had to put him out of action.

"He is in that thicket over on the hillside next to that big rock. I can see movement now and then," Joe said. "Set your sights at three hundred yards and about four clicks to the right to compensate for the wind. We'll have to trick him into coming out into the open. I'm going to stand on that old stump and pretend to be looking for him. I hope I present a tempting enough target that he'll come out for a shot at me. He'll have to show himself to get a round off. When I give you the word, everyone is to fire at once. Don't hesitate, or he'll get me for sure. Wait for my signal then let him have it. If anyone fires too soon," Joe cautioned, "he'll duck behind that rock and get away. We have to take him out, or he will pick us off one by one."

Forty rifles were trained on that one man, just waiting for him to show himself.

Joe crawled to the stump and then slowly got up, making himself a visible target. He watched as the sniper shifted his position to lift his rifle for another shot. When he was reasonably sure the sniper was visible, he shouted, "Fire!"

Rifles fired like thunder, echoing off the trees. The sniper fell forward and Joe figured the man was dead before he hit the ground. He sent Gabby to confirm that fact. Gabby came back carrying the man's rifle and ammo back to the camp, then he went back to cooking the viper. The men got on with the business at hand as though the incident with the sniper never happened. The meat finished cooking and they were hungry. It was as simple as that.

Gabby carried three large pieces of golden brown meat on a sharp stick, the meat sizzling, hot from the fire. A large portion of the rice and beans had been cooked in an empty coffee can. They gave that can to Joe and Louise to share. Each person received a small portion of black beans and just about a handful of the rice. This was the first hot food that they had in a long time. Joe had never eaten anything so tasty. It could have been that they were all so hungry. They had no eating utensils, so he and Louise drank the beans and rice from the can, passing it back and forth until they emptied it.

Gabby picked up the stick holding the snake portions. The smell of roasted meat and spices made him drool. He pulled off a couple of large chunks of meat off of the stick, handing them to Louise and Joe. She began to eat the sweet delicate offering, but Joe hesitated. All he could see was that monster of a snake slithering across the ground. He had always hated snakes and now he was expected to eat it? He didn't think so, but he bit off a small piece of the meat and had to fight the urge to gag. He didn't want to appear a coward in his men's eyes so he tried to chew the snake. It seemed like the meat grew bigger and bigger in his mouth and the more he chewed, the bigger it got. He swallowed the food and it slowly made its way down into his stomach. His stomach growled.

"Thank you for the kind offer," he told him, "but I'm afraid I can't get it down."

Gabby shook his head. "Sargento, you need to eat. This will help bring back your strength. You're weak from loss of blood and from hunger. You haven't eaten any real food for three days now."

Louise said a few words in rapid Spanish, gesturing for Gabby to go away. When he would have walked off with the meat, she grabbed hold of the stick and handed the meat back to Joe. "Try to think of it as a piece of fish. The taste is just about the same, only better because of the spices."

Looking at the charred piece of meat, Joe's stomach did a flip-flop. Just the thought of touching that thing sent chills up and down his spine. He knew it was psychological, but that didn't help much. He had eaten some pretty weird stuff while in training, but he wasn't afraid of cactus worms or field mice. He knew he needed the nourishment, and Louise was so proud of her catch that he didn't want to disappoint her.

"We need you, but you'll not be able to help us if you don't eat," she said.

Joe knew that. He had to overcome his fear. Even his stomach growled, begging him to eat that repulsive thing! He thought of the night in the bar with Mr. Bristol and the big juicy steaks that were served to the crew. He pretended the snake was a nice thick T-bone, and managed to swallow some of it. Actually, it tasted good. He began to eat with his old gusto and soon licked his fingers. Always a fast eater, he quickly finished. He started to think of himself as a guerrilla after all, beginning to feel that he was a part of the family.

"I know I'll see that thing in my sleep for years to come," he said. "But I admit that the old boy tasted mighty good."

After everyone finished they sat and listened to the battle raging on the beach. The distant thunder of shells and bombs as they exploded seemed to be never-ending. Each man seemed preoccupied with his own thoughts. They all knew they were beaten. Without the help of the American forces, they had no hope of victory.

"Louise, I'm going to break up the unit into small groups of two or three. They should be able to find their way out. I want you to go find some of your friends and family and hide until this blows over," Joe said. "Don't even look back. Save yourself. There's nothing else you can do for the others or for me. The men will be able to find a way to get back to their own homes. I'll be heading back home, too," he lied.

"No, Sargento. My place is with you. I will not leave you and you can't make me go." Her serious black eyes gazed into his as she flipped her long hair over her shoulder.

Why was she being so difficult? "Louise, you can't help me. I may end up in prison or be shot. You can't save me. But you can get away. You can send word to my family and tell them what has happened to me. I want them to know."

"I don't care. I stay. My job is with you and I'll stay and help you as long as I can. If I was in trouble, would you run away and save yourself…No, you wouldn't and I won't do it either. When that big old snake had a hold on me, you came and helped me even though you were terrified of him. You came back to help me. This is same thing. I will not run away."

"Okay, Louise," Joe said. "I guess your mind is made up. Let's try to get some sleep. I'm so tired I can't even think straight. Find out if some of the men will keep watch while we get some sleep."

"I'll talk to the men," she replied, but before she could carry out orders, they heard the sound of a helicopter. It was making a sweep of the wetlands.

"Chopper coming!" Joe shouted to the men. "It could be one of ours, but let's not take any chances. We'll make sure, before we show ourselves. Everyone take cover." He watched the chopper. It flew in circles, low over the swamp.

"That's one of Castro's choppers! Get down and stay still! The camouflage uniforms will help, but don't look up. They can see our faces," Joe said.

The chopper circled until it spotted one of the men too far out in the swamp for adequate cover. It hovered down and a man leaned out to shoot from the open door. Sergeant Joe watched as the young man stumbled and fell. He lay there motionless. The chopper pilot couldn't find a place to set down to recover the body, so he made two passes over the spot, and then flew away.

"Well, so much for that poor fellow," Gabby said sadly. "He never had a chance."

"They are looking for exiles, all right," Joe said, as the helicopter went out of sight.

When the coast was clear, the body came to life and moved quickly out of sight. The men cheered and hoisted the man up on their shoulders. They danced around in glee. Joe waited until they put him down to ask him, "Are you hurt?"

"Only my pride," he said, his white teeth gleaming when he smiled. For two tense hours, they waited for the chopper to return. Satisfied at last that the enemy had lost interest in the dead man, they relaxed.

"Sargento, I've talked to the men, and Sam and Ben say they can stay awake for a while," Louise said with a yawn. "We can sleep for a bit."

Taking a ten by twelve tarp and a coil of rope they had salvaged from one of the trucks, they tied the tarp to four trees to provide some shade and put two tents under it. They camouflaged it with some tree branches. It was time for some shuteye at long last. As Sergeant Joe spread a blanket on the ground in one of the tents, Louise yelled snake and laughed when Joe jumped back.

"Ha! Ha! You're very funny. Now behave yourself and get some sleep, before I give you that spanking I promised you earlier." Joe crawled into the tent and Louise stood outside watching him.

"May I stay with you, Sargento? I want to be with you."

"What will your friends think? We don't want to do anything to hurt your reputation. You can share my tent, but you'll have to go to sleep."

"I don't think that will be a problem," she said, stretching and yawning. She crawled into the tent dragging a blanket behind her. She reminded him of a little child, clinging to her security blanket.

"I don't care what anyone thinks," she said. "I'm afraid and want to be with you, Sargento."

In that small tent, they had no choice but to lie close to each other. Her body felt soft and warm as she snuggled up to him. Her strong perfume filling the still air, it was almost overpowering in the small tent, but he had gotten used to it. He slipped his arm around her and pulled her into the crook of his arm. He wanted to comfort her, but his body cried out for sleep.

She took his hand and held it against her as they drifted off to sleep. She mumbled, "The Americanos will come, just wait and see. They'll be here soon."

He was too sleepy to respond. He didn't want to admit it, even to himself, but he needed her as much as she needed him. Just holding her close was enough. He knew they were in danger, that capture or even death was looming, but at the moment none of that mattered. His body cried out for rest. He sank into a dizzy, intoxicating stupor. "When we wake up, we will make plans to move and find a better place to hide," he murmured above her head. "Somewhere safe, somewhere they won't find us, somewhere up in the mountains maybe, somewhere…" If they could evade capture, they might find a way to get home. He tried to concentrate on a plan, but he fell asleep and dreamed he was home and it was Christmas time. The snowflakes fell softly to the earth and he and Louise were sitting next to a huge Christmas tree. There was a fire in the fireplace.

CHAPTER SIXTEEN

Joe felt pain stab him in the ribs. He woke up with a start and moaned when another boot caught him solidly in the rib cage. The Cuban soldier kicked him again. The other soldiers crowded around them laughing and jabbing at them with the butt of their rifles. Their shouts rang in his ears. The tent had been removed while they slept and they hadn't heard a sound. Their captors were kicking them as they lay there. Joe desperately tried to shield Louise with his own body. Their tormentors started to beat them with clubs. He blinked his eyes and tried to focus, but everything was a blur, and the voices and laughter seemed to be coming from far away. Two of their assailants dragged them to their feet and the beating took on a new dimension. One soldier punched Louise, and was drawing his fist back to hit her again.

With a surge of anger, Joe went after the fellow managing to get in two or three good solid punches before they could stop him. Blood gushed from the soldier's broken nose. Pulling a rag from his pocket to hold over his twisted nose, the man screamed at Joe. He didn't understand a word the soldier said. Several of the soldiers pointed their weapons at Joe's head, so he broke off his aggression. He looked around for his men. Apparently the guards had fallen asleep and the soldiers had walked in and nabbed most of the rebels while they slept. The others, those who had managed to make a run for it, scattered to prearranged hiding places to wait for dark and see if they could do anything to help their captured comrades.

Where are the troops Bristol promised us? he wondered. *They had better hurry or we won't be alive when they get here.* The soldiers forced Joe and the other captives to build their own holding cages from what looked to be long gates, made of pipe and chain link fence. Guards prodded them along with the bayonets on their rifles to unload them from a truck and wire them together to make a small stockade. They crowded thirty-six people into the homemade enclosure. There was standing room only and they soon learned that touching the fence was a corporal crime and would get your hand broken with a rifle butt.

A group of men approached carrying two oil drums that had been welded together, end to end. The open ends had been fitted with grating made from steel rods. Some of the soldiers dragged Joe over to the iron maiden.

"No, I'm not getting in that thing," he protested, kicking a soldier in the knee while the others were holding his arms. The soldier yelped in pain, his leg broken at the knee-joint. Two of the others held him, while one used his rifle to hit him in the head, and then they stuffed him into the five and a half-foot prison. The strong smell of fuel oil inside the drum made it hard for him to breathe. He felt light headed and sick to his stomach.

They were taking no chances and shut him inside the makeshift sweatbox. He had already injured two of their comrades, so they thought it best to contain him. There wasn't enough room for him to move around in the confines of that small cylinder. His arms were above his head in an uncomfortable position and stuck out through the bars. They dragged and rolled the drum over to a corner of the enclosure. They made a privacy fence by stretching canvas over the fence and across the space of the corner.

"Why don't you just kill me and get it over with!" Joe shouted, his voice echoing in his own ears. The cage was not tall enough for him to stand, nor was it wide enough to allow him to sit, so he ended up crouching with most of his weight on his injured right leg. The afternoon sun blazed hot in the sky and the temperature inside the drum reached well over one hundred degrees.

Joe's lips became parched. His tongue felt like swollen leather. "Water! Give me some water!" he yelled. Two of the soldiers kicked the drum over onto its side, slamming him painfully to the ground.

"Stand him up again," said the leader. "He is a very important fellow and I don't want him sleeping on the job." He laughed, when he looked into the drum. "My name is Miguel. I think you have broken my nose... you will pay for that," he threatened.

Joe thought the man seemed to consider himself a self-styled demigod, patterning himself after Castro. He may have been an officer, but he was no gentleman. He strutted around the compound like he had a ramrod up his butt and he chewed on a cigar just like the Central American

Robin Hood as Castro was referred to by the New York Times, in their Man of the Year Issue. He had even taken to nibbling at the edges of his large black mustache, just like his boss.

Louise would go to the drum whenever they would let her. Dragging a hose from the water truck, she would let the cold water run down over Joe, washing off the blood and dirt from his body trying to give him a drink in the process. The water also helped in removing some of the oil residue.

Miguel had the cruelest eyes Joe had ever seen. They reflected pure hate and utter contempt for his prisoners. He showed little respect for his own men and they never made a move without his approval. They all seemed to be afraid of him and Joe figured they most likely had reason to fear him. He barked out orders and they obeyed without a word.

"Bring me that document," he ordered. "I think my new friends are ready to sign it now."

"Not on your life," Joe said, when they brought the document to him. "I ain't signing anything."

"You will sign. If not, you will die," Miguel said confidently, puffing on a cigar.

Louise said quickly, "Do not sign it, Sargento. As soon as they have your confession, they will kill you. Whether we sign it or not, they will kill us."

Joe thought that this would be an excellent time for the cavalry to come charging in, but he didn't hear any bugles. He watched from his hotbox prison as all the prisoners were lined up in a single file and asked to sign the confession.

"Sign this," Miguel insisted, but each man shook his head. They were systematically beaten and taken back to the wire cage as soon as they refused. Lastly, Louise and Joe were given the opportunity to sign. He handed the document to Louise and she began reading it aloud to Joe.

"We are working for the government of the United States of America, to overthrow...." Miguel backhanded her across the mouth. She staggered backward and fell down, her lip bleeding. As she struggled to get up, he kicked her in the stomach.

"I did not give you permission to read it," he said. "Only to sign it. Now do as you are told and sign."

She couldn't speak, her breath coming in short puffs. She tried to stand but found herself too weak. She shook her head, still not signing.

Miguel grabbed her long hair and dragged her across the rough ground and threw her down beside the drum prison. He shoved the paper through the bars and thrust it into Joe's hand. He ordered Joe to sign it. Joe couldn't understand what they were saying, but Louise had said no and that was good enough for him. He also shook his head.

In retaliation, Miguel grabbed Louise by the hair and pulled her to her feet, slapping her repeatedly in the face, knocking her off her feet each time he struck her. His men would pick her up and Miguel would hit her again and again. Her mouth was swollen and her eyes were turning black and blue.

An older man stepped up and confronted him. It sounded as if he was trying to stop Miguel from hitting her anymore. "She only interpreter and can not make him to sign," he said.

"If I were you, I would watch myself, Tony. You might find yourself on the other side of the wire with the rebels," Miguel said in a husky whisper.

Tony stood up to him. "I was with Mr. Castro when we defeated President Batista and took over the government of Cuba. I killed seven loyalist fighters with my own hands," the man said proudly. "I cut their throats on his orders, three men and four women. I'm not afraid to kill. However, this is different. She is no threat to anyone."

Miguel drew what appeared to be a US made Colt 45 and pointed it at his head. "I do not wish to hear your war stories, old man, and how brave you used to be." Tony gave up and backed down.

Miguel hit Louise in the face, then looked at Joe, a cruel smile twisting his face into the hideous monster he was. He hit her again. Miguel watched to see if he might be persuaded to sign the confession.

"She's just a kid!" Joe yelled at the top of his voice. "Leave her alone. Why don't you pick on someone your own size? Let me out of this tin can and try slapping me around. You worthless piece of swamp trash, face me like a man. You and me, one on one."

Miguel hit her in the face again and blood from her nose and mouth dripped down on her clothing. He could see this method wasn't working and decided to take a new approach. They let her loose to roam the compound for a short time. She staggered over to Joe's private prison.

"Sargento Joe. Is not so bad. I'm okay. The Americanos will come soon and save us. Just wait, you see."

Joe looked at her swollen, bloody face and rage welled up inside him. He knew no help was coming. He didn't know what had happened, but he had known for quite sometime they were on their own. They were all going to die. He feared for Louise. Sooner or later, they would remember that she was a girl, and then the real torment would start. He thought he would go out of his mind. He wanted to get his hands around Miguel's throat and squeeze until he suffocated him. He would take pleasure in feeling the life go out of that man.

"Louise, if I ever get free, I promise you that I'll make him pay dearly for this. I'll kill him. I swear it."

Miguel stood watching, chewing on that wretched smelling cigar. "Turn the drum so the brave American can see what is going to happen. I want him to see everything."

The men did as they were told, placing the cylinder in a sort of a half-leaning position against the fence. Taking out a large combat knife, Miguel honed it to a razor edge. He would sharpen for a while, and then look at Joe and then Louise, curling his upper lip into a lecherous grin.

"Don't sign that paper," Gabby called out from the cage. "They will kill us anyway. We die as free men."

"Bring me that free man," Miguel said. "I think we need to make an example." They dragged Gabby from the holding area and he stood valiantly alone in front of Miguel, a man on either side to see he didn't escape. "You don't look so much like a free man to me," he taunted. "Turn him around," he ordered. They spun Gabby around and Miguel grabbed a handful of material and tore Gabby's shirt down his back. He placed the glistening blade of the knife against Gabby's shoulder and slowly moved it in a sawing motion from one side to the other, peeling off wide strip of skin and flesh. The poor lad's knees buckled, but he didn't cry out.

The men holding him laughed and said, "Skin him like the frightened rabbit that he is."

Miguel did just that. Strips of skin hung from his back, arms and chest, but Gabby would not beg for mercy.

"Where is that brave old soldier?" Miguel asked. "The one who cuts the throats of both men and women. Bring him to me."

Tony was ushered to Miguel. "What do you want now?" he asked.

"Show us how it's done," he said. "Here is the knife and here is a free man. Show us how one cuts the throat of a free man."

Tony took the knife in his right hand with the blade extending along his forearm with the sharp edge out. He grabbed his victim by the hair and with a strike so sudden that it was hard to detect, made a pass across Gabby's throat. So quick was his cut that there was no blood on the blade.

Gabby didn't seem to know that he'd been cut and tried to talk, but his vocal cords had been severed and no sound came. A split second later, blood gushed from the gaping slit and he sagged to the ground.

"That is how you cut the throat of a free man, or any man," Tony said, looking Miguel squarely in the eyes. He handed the knife back and walked away.

Miguel began to hone the big knife as before. "Get rid of that," he said to some of the men who had witnessed the murder. Gabby's eyes were rolled back in his head and he had stopped moving. They dragged him out to the hillside and left him.

Louise screamed and screamed. "You killed him! Oh, my poor Gabby. Why would you do that? He was good and kind and you killed him."

Miguel ignored her and continued to hone the blade until he was satisfied with the sharpness of the weapon. He commanded two men to hold Louise by her arms. He took the knife and cut one of the buttons from her blouse. "You will sign now." He grinned.

"No!" Louise screamed.

He slowly continued to cut off her buttons one at a time. As each fell to the ground, Miguel would ask the same question.

"Now will you sign?"

She shook her head. "No," she said, as he continued to cut the buttons from her blouse until the last one fell to the ground in front of her. The blouse opened and revealed her undergarment. A rosary with beads and a crucifix of meticulously hand-carved wood hung from her neck. Louise began to pray in Spanish.

Joe didn't like the look in Miguel's eyes. He looked as if he had reached the point of no return. He had one thing on his mind, and it wouldn't matter if they signed now or not.

Louise saw the look, too. "Help me, Sargento," she pleaded.

Joe yelled and cursed Miguel, but he only laughed in contempt. Joe tried desperately to kick the bars in the end of the oil drums, but they didn't budge. He really couldn't get any leverage because he was in a crouched position. It stung his feet and the makeshift prison held him like an animal caught in a trap. "Let her go! She's just a child!" Joe screamed, but Miguel was beyond reason.

Slowly, Miguel cut away each garment until she stood naked and shivering in the heat of the day. Tony threw her a blanket and she wrapped it around her trembling body to protect herself from the stares of the hardened men.

"See how modest she is," Miguel taunted, "but that won't save her. Only you can save her, if you'll sign." He held up the paper.

"No, Sargento," Louise screamed. "Don't sign it. He kill us anyway."

Pointing to a spot on the ground, he ordered. "Put the blanket down there and lie down on it."

"No! I won't," she said, fear in her black eyes. She trembled uncontrollably.

"If you do not do as I say, I will cut three fingers from the hand of your sargento," he threatened.

It was not an idle threat. She had witnessed what he did to Gabby. This man was capable of the most despicable acts. She hesitated for a moment, and then complied.

Miguel came near to Joe and said in fluent English, "She is such a lovely girl, isn't she?" He laughed, the sound demonic. "Now, if you will excuse me, I have a date."

He went to the blanket and raped her. As he stood up, he stared with disbelief at the blood on the blanket. Glancing toward Joe, he grinned, "Thanks for saving her for me." He sneered like a blood-hungry animal devouring a carcass.

"Hernadaz, it's your turn," he told one of his men. He watched and smoked a cigar as one by one he instructed his men to molest her. They callously stole her gift. Each of those cruel men seemed to be trying to outdo the last in how badly he could treat her, showing what terrible things he could do to a young girl. They seemed to enjoy hurting and shaming her.

Joe heard her screaming for him. She kept calling for him to help her. There were so many of them that Joe lost count. Rage shook Joe's body and he wanted to kill each one of them with his bare hands. He vowed that if he got the chance he would show no mercy. He kept hearing her screaming for him to help. He kicked at the drums that held him secure. He knew he was losing his mind.

After they were finished with her, they went about their business as if nothing unusual had happened. One man, who had not touched Louise, came into the compound and put a blanket over her nude body.

"Take a little water from my canteen," he said softly, gently raising her head so she could take a small sip of water, trying not to notice when the water ran down her chin because her mouth was so swollen. "My name is Gabriel. I can't do much, but I'll help you all I can." Using his handkerchief, he wiped some of the blood from her face. "I feel so bad that this has happened to you. I have a daughter your age at home, but I'm not a brave man. I can't go up against Miguel." He wrapped the blanket around her shoulders gently. "Besides, he would kill me if I did."

"Please help me over there to where Sargento Joe is."

Gabriel looked like an animal caught in a trap. He wanted to help her, but he looked terrified. His eyes darted to the opening of the enclosure, to Louise and back again.

Hesitantly he said, "I better not. Miguel might catch us. He'd kill us both." Fear registered on his face. After some time, he couldn't refuse her cries and pleading. Holding her up, he half carried her over to Joe, and then he looked down into the drums and said in broken English, "She wants to talk to you, Sargento. I'll step back so I can't hear. I would like to help, but I am one man. What can one man do against so many? Try to hurry; they'll make me come out soon."

Joe asked, "If I sign that paper, will they leave her alone?"

"I don't think so. They all ran from the fighting on the beach and now they want to show how brave they are. They're drunk and they want to take out their anger on someone. You and the girl are just available targets."

Too weak to stand alone, Louise held onto the side of the drum. She started to speak in Spanish.

"Louise, in English."

It took her two or three tries before she could remember the words. Her jaw looked broken by the way it was swelling and turning black and blue. Some of her teeth had been knocked out, making it very hard for her to pronounce her words. "They took away my gift. Now I have nothing to give to my husband," she whispered, between the sobs of pain.

He knew she was talking about her virginity. She held high moral standards and he couldn't stand to see her head bowed in shame. He wanted to comfort her. "A gift is something you give away. You did not give it away. They stole it from you. Besides, your body is not the gift. You are. You are my gift, Louise. Do you understand?" He hoped so.

She tried to smile, but her mouth just twisted. "Thank you, Sargento. I want you to know my name." Before he could stop her, she said, "My real name is Marcia Cardona. I wanted you to know before we are killed. I know you won't tell."

"You shouldn't have told me. I'll do my best not to betray your trust. I'll try to forget your name, but I will never forget you." He could never forget her name. It burned into his memory and he wanted to hold her hand, but he couldn't get to her.

The men outside began to curse and yell, wanting their turn at Louise. Gabriel finally had to leave. Using his shirttail to wipe the tears from his eyes, he said, "God be with you." By pretending to join in the torture, he had given her some comfort. As he went out, he tucked his shirt into his pants, acting like he was getting dressed. Joe was grateful that he had found one man in Castro's Army that was humane.

Miguel had the men string a wire from the engine of the water truck to the compound, connecting it to a spark plug. "I want you to know what your girl friend will be feeling," Miguel said. Fastening the wire to the drum, he had someone start the engine. Each time that plug fired, it sent 12,000 volts of electricity surging through Joe's body. He jerked violently and clinched his teeth so tightly that he cracked some of them. Encased in metal as he was, any point of contact would snap a spark to a different part of his body. The charge shook his body and he convulsed. The water that Louise had poured on him before and his own perspiration made a good ground for the electricity. He lost all track of time and couldn't tell how long they left the wire on. It may have been only seconds, but it seemed to go on forever. He wanted desperately to die, to get away from the pain.

"Would you like some more, brave American liberator?" Miguel laughed.

"No, please!" Joe said his voice weak from fatigue. The pain had exhausted him. "Don't do that to her."

"Do you see this pen? It's the same pen that I was willing to let you borrow to sign my little paper, but you refused. Now I must find another use for it. Can you guess what I will do with it?" He twisted the ominous wire around its metal barrel five or six times and sauntered over to Louise.

Joe went wild. "Don't do that to her, you animal." He raved and he cursed and tried to get free from his prison. The welded hotbox held him prisoner. He knew firsthand how terrible it felt and wished that he could take it instead.

When Louise realized what he had in mind, she struggled to her feet to run, but Miguel punched her squarely in the face and she fell face down. She offered no further resistance as he inserted the pen like a suppository. She lay on the blanket with her arms extended along her sides, stiffly bracing for what she knew was coming.

"Shall I give the order to start the truck?" Miguel said with a smirk.

"If I get out of here, I'll wipe that stupid grin off your face, you sniveling coward."

Miguel held up his index finger and moved it in a circular motion a couple of times and the truck started. Louise began to shake uncontrollably as the electricity bit at her insides.

Louise screamed when the voltage hit her weakened body. She almost levitated off the ground at times. Her tormentor seemed to be enjoying the show and kept the engine running for a long time, at a very slow idle. Even after the wire was removed, her muscles continued to constrict, causing her to jerk and shudder with each spasm. Joe's arms ached to hold her and let her know that he cared.

Joe cried out, "Louise, you are the bravest person I have ever known. We'll make it somehow. Just hold on. They're trying to break your spirit, don't let them. Gabby was right, we're free and they can't steal that. Just keep holding on. We'll make it somehow. I know you aren't going to let them get by with this without a fight. I'd help you if I could. You must believe that." He knew that they had reached the end of the line, but wanted her to know that he cared.

With her body still wincing, Miguel raped Louise. She screamed when he brutally handled her. He tortured her until she told him her real name. He seemed to get a kick out of taking the last thing that was hidden from him.

"Cardona," he said, rolling the sound around on his tongue. "I knew a woman named Cardona. She worked for Batista. Do you know her?"

"My mother," Louise admitted in defeat, knowing from past experience that he would not let up on her until she told him the connection.

"Oh, yes. I remember your mother. You squeal like a little pig, same as her." He laughed as if it was all a big joke.

Joe thought there must be a special place in Hell for this man.

When Miguel had enough, he let the gang rape continue throughout the night. Louise cried and begged, but her pleading fell on deaf ears.

CHAPTER SEVENTEEN

Joe thought about his home back in Ohio. He thought about his parents and siblings. Would they hear of his death or would he be a missing person? Perhaps his lifeless body would show up on the six o'clock news. He even wished he could go back to that job he hated so much, digging holes in the ground, as Bristol had put it. He would like to put Miguel into one of those holes and throw Bristol in for good measure. The whole mission had been in vain. Joe came here because he wanted to make a difference, to have his life count for something.

He thought about Gabby. He had so much potential, yet his life was snuffed out to make a point. His killer showed no remorse. Joe didn't want to think about what was happening to that little girl out there in the dark. He tried to block the sound of her cries from his ears, but he would never be able to. They would haunt him for the rest of his life.

After countless hours, they had their fill of torturing Louise. She no longer looked like that pretty little girl he danced with at the club. She looked like a crushed flower.

They had satisfied their lust and went back to their drinking. Some slept off the liquor while others continued to drink. Several men came into the compound, bringing food and liquor for the victory celebration. They had defeated the rebel forces and were enjoying the spoils of war.

They left Louise on the shabby blanket, wet with her own blood as she sobbed and cried throughout the night. Standing was just too much of an effort. In the morning she crawled to the sweatbox, dragging the water hose behind her. She stopped several times when the convolutions would strike her body. She twitched involuntarily.

"You need water, Sargento Joe. I'm coming." Her voice sounded so weak that he could hardly hear her.

Cold water trickled down for him to drink and the cold water soothed his cramped body. Looking out between the bars, he hardly recognized the once beautiful young girl. Miguel and his men had taken a pretty girl, and transformed her into a battered, bloody, whimpering piece of flesh. Her face was swollen beyond recognition. Some of her teeth had been knocked out. Both of her eyes were black and one was swollen shut. Her beautiful, long, black hair hung half over her mangled face, tangled and matted with blood, dirt and vomit. One of her drunken rapists had become sick while assaulting her. The cool water flowed into the drum for only a few minutes when Miguel looked in on them.

He walked into the compound with another man. Miguel grabbed a fist full of black hair and dragged Louise back to the bloodstained blanket on the ground. She fell to the ground sobbing. Miguel pulled Joe's left hand out and slit his wrist, letting the blood spurt out on the ground. Each time Louise would try to help Joe, Miguel would knock her down.

Gabriel, the man who had treated her with kindness, came into the compound and asked if he could talk to her.

"Yes," Miguel said. "Tell her that her Sargento doesn't have much time. If she wants to save him, she had better sign it now."

"If you sign the paper, Miguel will let you help him," Gabriel told her. He turned to look at Joe. "I should let you bleed to death. If it hadn't been for you and your country, none of this would have happened."

Louise quickly agreed to his demands and said, "I sign for my Sargento." They brought that paper out again and she signed it. They had what they wanted and they let her go. She stumbled over to Joe. Finding the cut in his wrist, she kept her thumb firmly pressed into the artery, stopping the blood flow. One of the guards had been watching; he walked over, knocked her down, then walked on past. She struggled up once again, coming back to her task. She was so weak that she fell several times and each time the blood would gush again, but she managed to keep her thumb on his wrist until the bleeding stopped.

"It has stopped now...bleeding stop," she mumbled, as she slumped to the ground.

"Louise, can you hear me?" Joe asked, but she only cried and whimpered. He tried to talk to her, but she just rocked back and forth, retreating to a kinder place, a place where no one could hurt her.

He could hear her as she began to stir in the darkness. She had been curled into a fetal position in the mud and water that mingled with her and Joe's blood.

After two or three attempts to sit, she gave up and just lay there in the mud. Her sobbing had turned to a cry much like a newborn baby or a little rabbit caught in a trap.

"Just lie still and rest," Joe told her. "It's all over now. They will leave you alone. You signed their stinking paper."

The sun had just come over the horizon when Miguel began to shout commands, and ten of the prisoners, with their hands tied behind their backs, were marched out of the compound. Wanting to be sure that Joe could see it all, Miguel ordered the men to kick the barrel over onto its side. A short time later, he heard gunshots, then the screams coming from the hillside. The smell of gunpowder drifted across the compound hanging heavily in the air. Joe watched the grisly scene. The men were forced to kneel, and then shot in the back of the head. The death squad came back for the next group. The lust to kill had overtaken them. One of the guards had placed a bayonet on his weapon and as the prisoners were marched out, he lunged, sticking the bayonet into John's back. He struck with such force that the blade cut through his backbone, severing the spinal cord, leaving the poor man writhing in the mud and screaming, "Ayudame, Sargento!" (Help me sergeant.) His executioner struggled to retrieve the bayonet, but he was too drunk to pull it out. He just unhooked it from the rifle leaving the large knife sticking in the man's back. He then placed the rifle close to the back of John's head, finishing the job with a thirty-caliber bullet.

Miguel got angry. "That is not what I told you to do!" he shouted. He struck the guard in the face with the barrel of his pistol, knocking him to the ground. Blood splattered from his nose and mouth. Miguel kicked at him as he scrambled to get on his feet.

"You were in such a hurry to kill him. Now drag him out by yourself."

The drunken guard struggled to drag the body out with the rest of the executed prisoners. The murderer had trouble obeying because he was still almost too drunk to walk, and he had the beginnings of a horrendous hangover.

Now the holding area was empty, except for Joe and Louise.

Miguel ordered two men to drag Louise over to the blanket. They pulled her over the rough ground like a bag of potatoes. They threw her on the blanket and she landed face down. The only possessions the captors had overlooked were her rosary, that small flag pin that Joe gave her and the little onyx ring that still circled her finger. She had kept the pin hidden, clutched tightly in her hand. The rosary was still hanging from its chain around her neck. Louise took hold of the rosary and began to pray. Miguel watched for a moment before walking to the girl. He stood behind her, watching for a moment as she counted the rosary beads; he then walked in front of her, cutting her prayer off in the middle by stepping on her hand with the heel of his boot and twisting with a grinding motion.

The sickening crunch of breaking bones sounded loudly in Joe's ears as her hand and the rosary was ground into the dirt. A little whimper could be heard, so quiet if one hadn't been close it couldn't have been heard.

"I have been saving the best till last," Miguel said, looking at Joe. Taking out his USA made colt-45-caliber pistol, he placed the barrel about six inches from the back of her head and pulled the trigger. The big gun bucked twice in his hand as the sound echoed with an almost deafening roar. The bullets passed through her head and into the ground and her body jerked and quivered as life ebbed out of her.

The guards, who had been shouting and cursing, stopped in stunned silence at the sound of the shots and stared silently at Miguel. No one said a word. The girl died without a sound coming from her lips.

Miguel gave the small body one final kick with the toe of his combat boot to make sure she was dead.

Joe felt a strange sense of relief. They couldn't hurt her anymore. She was finally beyond their reach. He knew she hadn't felt that last kick. Joe sadly watched the guards lift her by the corners of the blanket, careful to not get her blood on their clothing, as they carried her out.

Grinning, Miguel turned to Joe. "Now it's your turn, American dog. You are not so brave now. You have tears in your eyes." He laughed that insane laugh. "You could not mind your own business. NO.... NOW you will die like the weakling that you are." He took aim at Joe's head and fired through the steel drum. Joe felt a sudden burst of pain and saw a blinding flash of light. He could feel himself going to sleep. He couldn't stay awake. He felt too tired to struggle, too weak to hold on any longer. It was so easy to let go. "This is what it's like to die," he whispered, as he embraced the blackness that swept over him.

They dragged him, still imprisoned in that little sweatbox, onto the hillside, leaving it beside the little blanket wrapped figure. They were in a hurry to get back to their drinking.

Miguel said to his men, "Just leave them there for now. Our commander, Mr. Castro, might come along and we want to show him how we took care of his enemies when we bring all these defectors to Havana. We'll all be heroes. They'll keep until we finish our celebration. I have called ahead for some trucks to haul this garbage. After our party we can load them onto the trucks and take them as a special gift to Mr. Castro."

CHAPTER EIGHTEEN

Sam and Ben took their position on the hillside under the cover of the bushes, in full view of the camp. They watched in horror as their comrades were marched out in groups and shot. They wanted to help their friends, but they were out-numbered. They watched for any sign of their Sergeant or Louise. They knew they had been captured with the others. Sam and Ben had been standing guard but had fallen asleep. They barely escaped when the soldiers found their camp and captured the sergeant, Louise, and the other exiles. Ben and Sam didn't have time to sound the alarm. All was lost. They ran into the swamp and hid for days. They finally mustered up enough courage to leave their safe haven to find out what had happened to the others. The loss of life staggered them. As they looked on, four men came over the knoll carrying something in a blanket, throwing it among the dead bodies. Terrified, they silently watched. After a short time the soldiers came back dragging a long cylinder made of two oil drums over the little hill. They dropped it then kicked it next to the blanket. Laughing, the soldiers went back to the compound.

"It looks as if they are all going back into their camp," Ben said. "I'm going to check to see if anyone is still alive."

"It is too late. They're all dead." Sam kept down so he wouldn't be seen if the soldiers returned. "We should leave here as soon as we can."

"You do as you wish, but I am going to see if anyone is still alive before I leave this place," Ben said with determination.

"All right. At least let me crawl up the hill to see what is going on in the camp first. We don't want unexpected visitors." Ben gave a nod. Sam carefully made his way to the top of the hill. The camp rang with victory shouts. The soldiers were still drinking.

Ben and Sam scrambled to check all the dead bodies. The enemy had done their work well. It didn't look as if anyone had survived the massacre. Giving up, they started to slip back into the swamp when they heard a noise. They paused and listened, fearful that a soldier had come back to loot and salvage anything they might have missed on their first inspection. They looked at each other when they realized the sound came from near the cylinder.

Sam started to walk back. "Someone is still alive. I heard something over there by those oil drums."

Ben followed Sam and stooped to open the blanket. "I think this is Louise," Ben said, noticing the long black hair that protruded from the bloody blanket. He pulled back the corner of the blanket and turned away quickly, gagging. He made the sign of the cross. "Oh, no! Look at what those animals did to her. They didn't have to do that to her. These men are animals. I can understand killing an enemy soldier, but not this."

Walking over to the blanket, Sam looked, and then quickly turned away. He began to cry and to vomit. He couldn't stop retching even when his stomach had emptied its contents.

They all loved and respected Louise.

"We can do nothing else for her," Ben said, looking around. "Let's find out where the noise came from and get out of here. This place reeks of death."

"It's the Sargento. He is in this thing." Sam peered into the prison. "Help me get him out of there." They pulled enough of the iron bars from their holes to open the top of Joe's prison and dragged him out of the sweatbox. "He is breathing. He is shot in the head, but it looks as if the bullet has only grazed him."

"Come on, Ben. Help me with him before they come back and find us. We must get him back to the place where the supplies are hidden. It won't take us long, now that we know where we are going."

Joe murmured, half-delirious, slowly gaining consciousness. He had a splitting headache and he could still hear the roar of the pistol ringing in his ears. Looking around, he tried to get his bearings. What had happened? Where was he? He shook his head to clear the cobwebs. He tried to get to his feet; staggering, he fell back to the ground. Fighting to clear his mind and think, he shook his head again and almost passed out from the pain. Suddenly, the horrible memories flashed through his mind. "Louise," he cried out.

They were so close to the camp that Ben and Sam tried to quiet him. The din from the camp had grown louder with yelling, cursing, and drunken laughter.

Joe wiped the dripping blood from his eyes with his sleeve. The past events played through his mind like a horrible movie. Only this was too real. He could smell the stench. He slowly stood up looking around him. He could hardly see through the cloud of flies and mosquitoes feasting on the bodies of the fallen. About forty men lay sprawled over the landscape, but where was Louise?

"Where is she?" he asked softly.

"Here, Sargento. She is over here." Sam pointed to the dirty blanket.

Joe stumbled to her remains, knelt down beside the blanket and uncovered her. He just sat there looking at her for a long time without saying a word. Shock had robbed him of all feeling. He couldn't cry. Tears would come later.

"We must go, Sargento. We have stayed long enough. There is nothing we can do for her."

"I can't leave her like this. She saved my life."

"We saved your life, too, Sargento," said Sam. "And if we do not leave this place, it will cost us ours."

Joe could not leave her like this. He could not walk away and leave her to the swarms of flies feeding on the dead bodies. He gently wrapped her lifeless body in the old, blood-soaked army blanket, tightened and secured it with belts that he took from three of the murdered men. He bound them in such a way that the belts would hold the blanket in place. Looking to his left he spotted the bayonet still sticking in John's back. Two or three quick jerks and it came free, leaving about one-half inch of bone on the point.

Placing her on his shoulder, his blood mingling with hers on the blanket, he started walking toward the swamp, away from the carnage on the hillside. He remembered her words. She wanted to be buried on a hill where the sun would shine and the earth would be warm. It was the least he could do for her. She had done so much for him.

Ben shook his head. "You can't carry her. You are weak. You must leave her here and save yourself."

"I want to give her a decent burial."

"But there is no time for such foolishness. She doesn't know," said Sam. "We have to get away from here as soon as we can if we are going to live."

"I know." Joe struggled to wade through the swamp with the heavy burden flung over his shoulder. He would not leave her. He ignored the protests and urgency in their voices. Slowly they began wading through the swamp, looking for a dry place to dig her grave. He trudged through water to his chest at times, but he held her as high as he could to keep the stagnant water from soaking into the blanket. If it got waterlogged, it would become too heavy to carry. Weak and exhausted, he pushed on.

An alligator, drawn by the smell of blood, suddenly appeared, swimming about ten feet in front of Joe, it's huge jaws open for an attack. Quickly, Joe placed her body on an old tree limb and went for the reptile with the bayonet. Ben came to his rescue with the M-1 rifle he had kept, shoving the muzzle of the rifle into the 'gator's mouth, and pulled the trigger three times as fast as he could shoot. The reptile's mouth had closed on the rifle muffling the sound of the shots. The three bullets killed the large reptile. Joe recovered his burden and stumbled on; he just had to find the best place possible for her final resting-place. Throughout most of that day and into the night, they kept on.

Sam and Ben were angry and tried to persuade him to put her down. They spoke in broken English and Spanish and he only half understood what they said. He understood the body language and tone of voice, but he still carried her, slowing down their progress and chances of escape. He had to do something for the valiant girl who had saved his life. They could have had a life together, but now all was lost. He refused to turn her over to the flies and animals of the swamp.

She had looked up to him as a leader and her protector; but in the end, he could not defend her against her attackers. It stripped him of his manhood. He had never felt so helpless in his life. He still hoped for a chance at Miguel.

He planned to give her a decent burial and it didn't matter how much the men protested. He couldn't understand much of what they were saying anyway. She had been his interpreter and the only means he had of communicating with his men. He had picked up a few words of Spanish and some of them had learned a little English, but not enough to really carry on a conversation. Still, he understood enough to know they wanted him to leave her. He had failed one mission, but he was determined to complete this mission for her sake.

He spoke to the dead body hanging over his shoulder. "If I ever get out of here, I will kill each of them." That thought kept him going and gave him strength. He might not get all of them, but he would kill as many of them as he could. If he died in the attempt, so be it. What was life without her?

He found a spot where the ground was fairly dry and soft on a little hill. It was in the sun and there were flowers growing nearby. He took the battered bayonet, the one they had used to kill John, and began to dig. Brushing back the rotting vegetation with his hand, he chopped at the red earth. The others watched him for a while, and then shamefully joined in the digging, scooping the dirt out with their hands as he loosened it with the bayonet.

Suddenly, Joe felt weak. His head began to nod as he fought the darkness that was threatening to overcome him. Ben stopped and watched him for a moment. They motioned for him to sit down.

"Sit down, Sargento," Ben said. "We'll finish." The two men continued to dig the shallow grave.

Joe sat alone with his sorrow. He opened the blanket for one last look. Her right hand still clutched the rosary. The crucifix was crushed and the bones were sticking out of some of her fingers where Miguel had ground them into the dirt. Gently prying open the fingers of her left hand, he found the onyx ring still circling her finger, and the little flag pin, the one he had given her that night at the club. He took them, pinning the flag on the collar of his shirt, but left the rosary with her. He wanted to keep the pin and ring, as something they had shared together.

Her rosary and that small US flag insignia were precious possessions and had meant so much to her that she clung to them even in death. He pulled her into his arms holding her until they finished digging the grave.

Tears started to slowly bubble to the surface, running down his bloody cheeks. He couldn't let her go even when the men had the grave ready to receive her. He just didn't want to let her go, because he knew that he would never see or touch her again.

"It is time," Ben said gently, taking her from his arms. He gently lowered the blanket into the soft earth. He crossed himself saying a few words in Spanish.

Sam handed Joe a poncho to cover her. Joe tenderly tucked her in like a baby, and then turned his back. He just couldn't bear to watch them cover her with dirt. When they were finished, Sam and Ben left him alone.

He sat staring at the mound of earth, not seeing a grave, but remembering the beautiful young lady whose deep brown eyes sparkled with excitement and laughter. He lost himself in a bittersweet memory of that happy time when they first met and the way she tried to teach him to dance; the way she had looked up at him so trustingly. That cut like a knife. He had failed her miserably. He pushed the guilt away and lost himself in happy memories; the way her long, black hair blew in the wind when they took a drive that night long ago. Each recollection tore at his heart, reminding him of what he had lost.

After awhile, he took the bayonet and began to carve on the large log they had rolled into place to make a headstone of sorts. Working hard most of the day, these are the words he carved for her.

*****

EPITAPH

HERE LIES MARCIA, THE BRAVEST AND THE MOST ADORABLE LITTLE SOLDIER TO HAVE EVER SERVED IN ANY ARMY ANYWHERE.
*****

His grief turned to anger and his anger to rage. Now the only thing he wanted was to get his hands on Miguel. If Miguel had shot Louise without all the torture, it would have been bad enough, but this was quite another matter. He wasn't human. He wasn't even good enough to be considered an animal. Animals kill for food in order to survive. Miguel killed for political gain and for the sheer pleasure of it. He enjoyed the power he had over the lives of other people. Killing Miguel would be just retribution and a gift to society. He would be doing people a favor. He couldn't be left alive to do that kind of thing to other young girls. Torture was a craft to him and one that he practiced proficiently. Joe knew he had to find a way to stop him. He had killed Louise and her mother. He had done despicable things to both of them. Joe wondered how many notches he had on his belt. Joe wanted him to pay. Joe was going to send him to Hell where he belonged. That thought gave him a reason to live.

After some time, Ben said, "Sargento, it's time to go. We can't stay here any longer. We must leave now."

Joe heard the urgency in his voice. Keeling down beside the grave, Joe whispered, "Adiós mi amor." Raising his voice, he said, *"Bueno por mi amigo le veré en cielo."* {Good-bye, my friend. I will see you in heaven.} He wasn't sure that he had said it exactly right, but he had heard the others say it and he knew what it meant.

Ben stood nearby and heard him whisper it to Louise. He said it out loud, so all could hear and the three of them joined in and repeated it, *"Bueno por mi amigo le veré en cielo."*

Joe looked back once at the grave. Ben and Sam wanted to get as far away from the soldiers as possible, but Joe wanted to go back. Being the leader, they finally resigned themselves and followed his command. Joe followed Ben and Sam along the rim of a low ridge to a spot where they could watch the enemy's camp. It was quiet. They had apparently partied all night and now most of them were sleeping it off. Suddenly, Joe heard a noise. They took cover and watched as two men came toward them, grumbling as they walked. They were guards sent out to secure the knoll, and didn't seem happy that they had been ordered to duty while the rest slept off the victory celebration.

Joe tapped Ben on the shoulder and pointed to him and then to the soldier who had stopped to relieve himself. The other man kept walking until he was near Sam's position. Sam gave Joe a thumbs-up and pulled out his knife, holding it so that Joe could see it. Joe gave them a nod and they neutralized the guards without a sound. They continued on until they found a good spot to observe the enemy encampment. Joe's belly growled so loud that he was afraid Castro would hear it all the way to Havana.

"You need food. We found C-rations, guns and water not too far from here," Ben informed him.

"Go. Bring what you can," Joe said with a combination of words and sign language. He was so weak he would only slow them down. "I," he said, pointing to himself, "will stay here," he said, pointing to the ground. "Watch the camp," he said, aiming two fingers at his eyes, then at the compound.

The two young men nodded and headed out. They seemed more confident, now that Joe had taken control.

While they were gone, Joe watched the camp, trying to get an accurate count of the soldiers coming and going. He thought he counted over three hundred before he finally gave up. He thought about how they could make life interesting for Miguel and his buddies.

Miguel and his men were drinking and having a high old time. They were enjoying their victory and there seemed to be a never ending supply of food and rum. Joe had never witnessed a camp so out of control. He had been in the army and sometimes a few soldiers would have a bit too much to drink and would engage in activities that landed them in the brig. However, here it seemed all the men were three sheets to the wind. He was accustomed to men drinking, but usually someone, mainly MP'S, would keep things from getting out of hand. As he watched, a fight broke out and the shouting and cursing increased.

"I hope they kill each other," he said aloud.

The fight lasted almost an hour, with the onlookers cheering and goading the two opponents. It turned into a tag team match, then a full-blown free-for-all, with several of the men rolling around on the ground, apparently too drunk to stand. One fellow came forward with a knife and started swinging wildly, but someone hit him on the head with a piece of firewood and he quieted down. As soon as one fight would end, another would break out. Finally, someone in charge came in and with a few well-placed kicks, scattered the combatants in all directions.

Joe watched intently, knowing the more they drank the better his chance would be of getting a few of them. Someone would pay for what they did to Louise. He watched Gabriel leave the enclosure carrying a bottle of rum. He passed so close to Joe that he could smell the liquor. He could easily have killed the old man with one thrust of his bayonet, but he remembered the kindness he had shown to Louise, even at the risk of his own life. He let him pass by. If it had been any of the others, he would have killed them without regret.

Gabriel was in a bad way. He had been drinking heavily from his bottle of rum, perhaps to help him forget the carnage he had witnessed He staggered and reeled as he sought a solitary place to drink. He stopped under a tree and sat on the ground, away from the celebrating He took the last swig from the bottle, and then hurled it at a nearby tree with all his might.

He started to mumble in a drunken stupor. "Dirty Americans. Why can't they leave us alone? That poor little girl. Miguel had to do what he did to protect our sovereignty, but why did that young girl have to pay such a high price. Why can't the Americans just leave Cuba alone? It's none of their business that Castro is running things. We're not all like Miguel and his men. We don't want to hurt anybody. We just want them to leave us alone. Why can't they see that?"

Gabriel leaned back against the tree. "What is happening? I don't know," he mumbled out loud. "I am just a soldier taking orders. Why did that girl have to die like that? It was her fault. She shouldn't have had anything to do with the horrible American. I don't know." He closed his eyes. "I just want to go home and leave this dirty place."

Gabriel opened his eyes. "So many dead bodies. So many brave young men, all Cubans, except for that one American devil. Why did he come here?" Gabriel undid the flap on his holster drawing his side arm. "I would shoot all the Americans if I could." He looked at the pistol for a long moment, and then cocked the hammer, trying to decide. He placed the muzzle into his mouth and pulled the trigger. No one even noticed the sound of the shot.

Most of the area was covered with water and underbrush, so the soldiers had bunched up to take advantage of the dry ground. They didn't think there was any danger. Only a handful of rebels had escaped and were probably miles away.

They drank and laughed as if they didn't have a care in the world. They didn't know that Joe watched from a safe distance and that he honed the bayonet until it had a nice keen edge. He continued to work on the blade for the rest of the afternoon as he watched them come and go, bringing more liquor and food.

"Eat, drink and be merry boys, for tomorrow you die," he said in a low voice.

He could smell the aroma of roasted meat and sweet potatoes coming from the camp. His stomach growled with hunger. Even the rice and black beans smelled good. He was so hungry he would have eaten a piece of snake meat and not complained.

Dismissing his hunger, he looked at a fuel truck parked about halfway up the hill. That could be just the ticket, the way to get some of them. He started to devise a plan. The more he thought about it, the more certain he became that it might work. There would be more than pork roasting in that camp if he pulled it off. If he could just get that thing rolling down the hill somehow causing it to explode, the resulting inferno would wreak havoc on them and would certainly kill some of them. He figured by the time the Cuban soldiers regrouped, he and his army of three could run away to fight another day.

The army had placed their tents in a semicircle with some on each side of the road. They built a huge bonfire in the center of the encampment. Joe added it up; one gas truck plus one campfire equals a heck of a big explosion. There was deep water on either side of them and a good distance beyond. They had placed themselves in a trap without ever knowing it. Defensive maneuvers were the furthest thing from their minds. They probably figured no one had the guts to attack them.

Joe laughed. If he didn't die from hunger pangs, he would send them a birthday cake tonight, a five thousand gallon one complete with candles. He knew that he would forfeit his life, but by that time, he had lost the will to live. If he could hold on long enough to get some of those butchers, he would be satisfied. He considered his life for twenty or thirty of them an even trade. He couldn't ask Ben and Sam to go along with him on this, because the odds of survival were slim to none. They could help him set up the surprise party, and then clear out. He would take it from there. He crouched on the ground, peeking over the top of the hill. He had been in one position for so long that he got a cramp in his right leg and almost cried out in pain. Still, Joe maintained his position and continued to watch.

Under his watchful eye, Miguel had his second in command post three guards. He stationed one at the gasoline truck, one about fifty yards from it at the foot of the hill next to the ammo truck and the third one stood near a group of trees at the south end of the camp so he could keep an eye on the road.

He had just about given up on Sam and Ben, thinking they might have weighed their options and decided to go home. He hoped they had. He had lost nearly every man. Still, he wondered if he could pull this maneuver off alone. He might have to.

The sun went over the hill and Joe hunkered down for the night. They came so quietly that Joe didn't know they were back until he felt a hand on his shoulder. He startled.

"Ben, you just about scared the life out of me." Joe smiled, relieved to see them, "Did you find any weapons or ammo?" He examined the things they had brought back to him. Some rusty old rifles, some corroded ball ammo, and a few cans of Spam. He looked at the guns and said, "So this is what those pilots and crews have been risking their lives to deliver." He sighed. "Well, it's better then nothing." There were some knives and some fine wire for making garrotes. He picked up the greatest prize of all, a carbine with a working sniper-scope. It could be used to watch the movements of the enemy at night. It didn't function as well as he would have liked, but he wasn't complaining. He was happy to get it.

"We brought back all we could carry and left the rest hidden in the swamp," Sam said.

After Joe filled them in on his plan, Sam gave him detailed directions to the hidden stash. They agreed to meet at that location if any survived the ambush.

Ben handed Joe a can of the Spam and he ate like a ravenous wolf, eating with his fingers, the meat and fat clinging to his fingers, which he licked off, savoring each speck of food. He drank a quart of water. His stomach settled down. With his hunger appeased, he turned his attention to the task at hand. Taking some of the wire, he twisted it into two garrotes, wrapping them into two small bundles. He put one of them into his right back pocket and the other into his right front to keep them from getting tangled. His left hand was swollen and sore from the cut on his wrist, a gift from Miguel. He worked his fingers back and forth trying to make a fist, being careful not to start the artery bleeding again. Ripping a strip of cloth from his shirt, he used it as a pressure bandage for his wrist, wrapping it tightly and bringing it down around his thumb to help hold it in place. He had to support and protect his injured wrist from the wire of the garrotes, to give him more of an edge.

To Joe's surprise, two men, who had been watching from a distance, slipped in from the underbrush. One was Marco, a short, dark-skinned man with a bushy mustache. The other was someone who needed no introduction. Joe immediately recognized Carlos, the same fellow who had challenged Joe for the affections of Louise. They had managed to escape when the soldiers had sacked their camp and they still had their weapons.

"Do you remember me, Mr. Big Shot Sargento?" he asked, with a dejected grin.

"Well, I see that you are ready to have your butt kicked and I would love to do it for you, but I'm right in the middle of a war and don't have time right now," Joe said, returning his smile. Neither one really felt like smiling, they were both still grieving for Louise.

"What can we do to help?" Carlos asked. Both of the newcomers spoke pretty good English and explained that they had fled when the raiders hit the edge of the clearing. In the confusion, they made good their escape and dashed into the swamp.

"Glad to have you aboard," Joe said with his signature smile.

"Do you have any food?" Carlos admitted they were hungry. "We have been so scared that we have been on the run for two days and haven't eaten. We grew tried of running like timid rabbits and came back to see what they were going to do with the others."

"Did you see?" Joe asked.

"We saw enough," Marco answered bitterly. "What can we do to send these black hearted vermin to Hell? Do you have a plan?"

"I sure do, but first eat and then we will discuss it."

Sam and Ben took the best of the old M-1 rifles, cleaned, and lubricated them. They had a couple of hours to get ready. The rifles were in sorry condition when the boys started working on them, but within the span of a half-hour, they were standing tall. Cleaned and oiled, they looked new. They had no bore brush, so they had to pull an oil-soaked rag through the barrels. They used a bit of the fine wire to clean out the gas ports. That tiny hole was a very critical part of the M-1. If plugged, it could cause the rifle to recoil hard enough to break a man's shoulder. They couldn't test fire the weapons knowing the sounds of the shots would alert Miguel's butchers and bring them down on their heads and they would have lost the element of surprise. They adjusted the sights to the combat setting of two hundred yards, and then waited for darkness to settle in.

Checking the ammo, they looked at each bullet individually to make sure it fit snugly into the shell casing and wasn't damaged or bent. Once in the dark, having a bad round jammed in the chamber could mean the difference between life and death, success or failure, so they were taking no chances. A loose cartridge may have gotten moisture inside it and the damp power would not fire.

While the men were eating, Joe sat down next to Carlos and said,

"I know how you felt about Louise and that you were only concerned for her well-being. I loved her, too. We'll never know how it would have played out. You're a good man and I am glad that you cared about her."

"Thank you, Sargento. I see now that you also had her best interest in mind." He bowed his head, lost in his own thoughts. He lifted his head. "It was you she loved. She told me don't be mad at you, and that neither of you could help how you felt. I went to see my father after I left here, and he said I should let her go, so I was going to release her from her father's promise that she would marry me." They sat in silence and ate. They rested, trying to regain their strength. Joe asked them to not let him sleep for more than an hour or two, but they didn't wake him until about 0300 hours. He almost felt like his old self again when he awoke.

While their Sargento slept, the men busied themselves by cleaning the rifles of Marco and Carlos and field stripping Joe's carbine and checking the action. They cleaned the glass of the scope and made sure it was battle ready. The men worked to head off any unforeseen problems. Taking care of last minute details, each man did his job to the best of his ability. They spoke softly so as not to awaken Joe.

"What are our chances?" Marco asked. "You know this Sargento better than we do. Can he do this thing?"

Without looking up, Ben said, "If anyone can do it, he can. He is not like other Yankees. He loves the Cuban people, and, as you can see, he is ready to lay down his life for us."

"I do not understand it. Why did he not stay at home where he was safe? I sure wouldn't risk my life for strangers."

"I think he loved Louise so much he would have gone anywhere to help her, and to make her happy," Carlos injected. "He will probably die this night and if I must also die, I want it to be alongside of a brave man," Carlos said.

"No one will remember. No one will know," said Marco.

"I will know," Sam said.

"And I," said Ben. "I will know that we did our best."

"Me too," said Carlos. "I am willing to die for Cuba."

"Then, so am I," Marco said. "Who knows, someday they may sing a song about us. The Heroes of the Revolution." They all laughed.

CHAPTER NINETEEN

They shook Joe awake. "It is time to destroy the destroyers, Sargento," Ben said. "Tell us what to do." Carlos, who spoke almost incomprehensible English, working hard, managed to interpret most of the conversation. Joe was beginning to understand a little for himself and that helped.

Even after getting some rest, Joe still felt a little weak and tired, but it was time to get this kamikaze mission on the move. Sam stayed close to Joe and although he could speak very little English, they seemed to be of one mind. They communicated well without words.

Marco had a good grasp of Joe's language, but he was a newcomer and Joe wasn't sure how he might react under fire. He placed the new men on top of the hill behind some trees and rocks where they had a good view of the camp. He told them to keep watch and to give them covering fire if they needed it.

"If it looks like we have a chance to get away, start shooting and keep shooting until you are out of ammo or all of them are dead. Either way, then head for the hills and don't look back," Joe said. He shook hands with Ben and Sam and said, "Vaya con Dios." They had forged a strange bond and the hardships had drawn them closer together. Joe asked them once more, "Are you sure you want to do this? If you want to leave, I won't think less of you."

"We did run, Sargento. Not feel good," said Carlos. "We will not run anymore." The others agreed.

"Good men." Joe felt privileged to know them. "I am proud to have served with you."

Ben said, "Sargento, we cannot go away and leave this thing unsettled. We know that we may die and that the chances of us getting many of them are very slim, but we must try. We must make them pay for what they did to our kinsmen and Louise. We have no choice, but to stay and be men." Carlos translated as fast as Ben spoke.

Sergeant Joe made up his mind that if he got the chance he would not show mercy to Miguel and the swine he commanded. He would kill with extreme malice and without regret. They had succeeded in changing him into the kind of beast he hated in them. He wanted to kill as many of them as he could before they got him. He didn't think he would live and get back to America. He knew in his heart that he would never see home again.

He wished he knew how to pray. This would be his last chance to make things right with God and he longed for the chance to see his family. He believed there was a God, but didn't know if God could hear his prayer. He had never gone to church or Sunday School. He had never prayed. He didn't have any religious training to fall back on, but the other men, being Catholic, had begun to bless themselves and to say their rosary. Joe felt that he ought to say something, so he bowed his head along with all the rest and prayed.

"Lord, You know what kind of man I am, and all of the things that I have done. I hope that You will cut me a little slack. It looks like I'll be seeing You in a short time, so try and give me a break if You can. Ah... thanks."

Starting out on their suicide mission, they understood they wouldn't be coming back. They planned to do as much damage as possible. Using the sniper scope mounted on his carbine, Joe easily located the three guards. They would have to be taken out before the action could really get underway. He carefully chose his avenue of approach, noting hazards such as dead branches, thorn bushes, and anything that might alert the sentries. Once Joe knew the lay of the land, he started to advance slowly, painstakingly, so as not to make a sound. He moved like a cat stalking its prey. The extra training from Yoko, and Tamara, and their friends in South America, came into play now and he was able to slip into the compound. He used an old stump for a reference point and moved in on the first guard at the south end of the camp. That one was in the best place to spot any activity and could see the other two guards from his post, so Joe had to put him out of commission first. This is what Joe had trained to do back at Breckenridge. That wise old Colonel Polk had taught him the tactics he would need to eliminate these fellows. He pushed the thought away that he was taking a human life. Moving on the wet soil and rotting foliage, he tried to avoid the muddy places. The sucking sound of a boot being pulled from the mud could warn a man of his approach. No matter how carefully he chose his course, his feet kept sinking into the mud with every step, pulling at his jump boots, and almost causing him to cry out from the pain in his wounded legs. Several times his boots made that sucking sound, but the guard was feeling the effects of the party and was still half drunk. He had propped himself up against a tree and was nearly asleep.

Joe slipped in from behind and quickly reached around the man's throat with his left arm to keep him from calling out. Pulling him backwards and using the bayonet, he plunged it deep into his rib cage. He made his first cut just under the shoulder blade, opening up a great gash. It sliced through his lung and blood gushed out of the wound. He pulled the man against his chest to muffle the gurgling noise of his breathing, and then reaching around to the front, cut his throat. The surprised soldier sank to the ground like a deflated balloon.

It amazed Joe that he had gotten this far as he went for the next sentry. He found him leaning against a tree, much as the other, still in a drunken stupor. Once on firmer ground, Joe could move more easily. Coming up behind the number two sentry, he took one of the garrotes from his pocket. He managed to get it around his enemy's throat and with a twisting and jerking motion, he yanked it as hard as he could. Turning until his back was against his foe, he bent forward and lifted the man's feet off the ground. He held him there until he stopped thrashing around. The wet blood ran down his back from the severed jugular. The man's struggling had caused the fine wire to bite deeper into his throat and his heart pumped blood out of his body at an accelerated rate. Joe felt the life drain out of the man. He felt no pity. Only hate and disgust. Dragging his lifeless body back into the brush, he quickly hid it from view. He stopped for a moment to consider what he had done. He had snuffed out two lives in less then ten minutes. He was drenched with the blood of his victims. The smell gagged him and he wanted to vomit. He reminded himself that these were the same men who had raped and tortured Louise. He didn't feel remorse. He likened it to killing a deranged and dangerous animal. Fighting was not new to him, but killing was something he had never done. This was no John Wayne movie. This was real life and real death, brutal, ugly, and savage. He pushed it from his mind. He had a job to do. He had to kill Miguel and his men. If he got rid of them, he would save countless lives. He would deal with the harsh reality of it later, if he managed to survive. He knew Miguel would never stop. He had to be stopped or else he would continue to kill and rape. Joe felt that it was up to him to see that that didn't happen.

There was one more guard to take out before they could get to that gasoline truck. Joe stopped for a moment to rest. The adrenaline flowed, giving him an edge he had never experienced before. His mind and actions were razor sharp. He got up and took the last garrote from his pocket, his hands shaking so badly he could hardly hold on to it. He stood absolutely still for what seemed an eternity. Mentally prepared, he moved on to the last sentry. The orange glow of the large campfire made ghostly shadows behind him and outlined the guard's form as he stood beside the gas wagon. Just as Joe moved in for the kill, the man arose, pulling himself up by the truck's fender and started walking around, holding on to the truck for support. Leaning and staggering up against the truck fender, he began to make preparations to relieve himself. He had trouble with the zipper and his coordination was off. Joe knew if he waited a while, this fellow would settle himself back into his routine and it would be lights out. So. Joe hunkered down to wait. While he waited, he thought about Louise. She had been so young and childlike in her ways and yet so very beautiful. He thought back to that night when they danced and how she had looked up at him, her eyes sparkling with pleasure and excitement. He closed his eyes and imagined he could see the sunshine reflecting from her coal black hair as it fell over her shoulder. She was boarding the boat that would take her to Cuba and he turned for one last goodbye. She stood next to the railing and waved to him. He remembered her parting words. "I will see you soon, my Sargento." He smiled. Then a ghastly picture of her mutilated body flashed before his eyes and his smile faded. This soldier standing before him had caused her a great deal of suffering and shame before she died. Now he would pay for what he had done. The longer he thought about it, the more his hatred took control. He gritted his teeth. It hurt. He hadn't wanted any part of this. He had been forced into it and then abandoned; tossed out like a worn-out shoe, expendable.

Nevertheless, he was still alive while most of his unit was dead. He almost let guilt consume him. He should have been better organized, made better use of his training, rotated the men so that some of them would have been alert enough to stand on sentry duty. He should have – could have – would have, and the thoughts raced through his mind condemning him. On hindsight, he thought he should have left the swamp and fled into the hills with his little band of guerrillas. In the mountains, they might have had a better chance to survive. He shoved the thoughts away like so much trash.

As Joe watched, the guard's head began to nod. It was only about fifteen minutes before he went to sleep, but it seemed like hours. The soldier's head wobbled, then sank slowly. Creeping up behind him with the garrote in hand, he let the loop of wire drop over the man's head, and then yanked it tight. He struck with such force, that it cut through the jugular and blood pumped out with each heartbeat. His hands came up, clawing at his throat. He desperately tried to free himself, but Joe applied more force. Joe was so scared that he turned with the wire over his shoulder and jerked on it again and again, until he heard the sharp crack of bones as they broke. He had cut clear through the man's neck, decapitating him. The head fell at his feet amid the shadows of the campfire. Startled, Joe jumped back. The warm blood flowed down his arm. He could see the man's mouth was still moving, trying to say pointless words, words that no one could hear. The unseeing eyes were open wide, staring at nothing. Joe watched in horror for the two or three minutes it took for the movement of the head to stop.

He couldn't believe that he could do that to another creature, much less a human being. He no longer knew himself and it scared him worse than dying. The mouth was no longer moving, but the headless body was still thrashing around. It reminded Joe of a chicken with its head cut off, blood spurting from the stump of its neck. If this had been a scene from a war movie, everyone would be eating popcorn and cheering for the star, but this was real life and Joe felt more like a murderer then a hero. It was like something out of the Twilight Zone. He had become detached from himself and it seemed like he was watching someone else do the killing.

He just couldn't do this. He hadn't been raised to kill another human being. But this was war and men did the unthinkable.

He knew he would die. It was a matter of time. He had to get Miguel before it happened. He signaled for Sam to come drive the truck. Sam came running and Joe started to climb to the top of the huge gas tanker.

He was going to ride *shotgun* on top of the rig, while Sam drove it right into the campfire. It would all be over in one giant explosion.

"Hold it, Sam," he said, as he looked at the nozzle attached to the end of the hose. It was badly dented, bent, and made of a very soft brass. "Do you think we can smash this thing?"

"You betcha," Sam said. "It spray mucho plenty."

"That's the idea," Joe said as they unwound the hose and stretched it out until it reached a big rock. Sam placed the brass nozzle on it and held it secure as Joe beat it flat with another rock, forming a sprayer of sorts. The slotted opening was so small that when they started the small pump engine, gasoline went shooting over a hundred feet.

They figured that as soon as the soldiers heard the pony pump, they would be all over them in a heartbeat, but they paid no attention to it. Perhaps they thought it was a generator and didn't come out to investigate. Ben gave Joe and Sam a thumbs up signal, and then he kicked the chunk of wood that had been placed under the rear wheel of the big truck to keep it from rolling. With the log removed, the gas tanker began to roll. Joe manned the hose. Sam drove the tanker and Ben clung to the window post with his left hand, holding his rifle in his right hand. They began to spray gasoline over the entire camp. The pungent smell of the high octane Sunoco Extra filled the predawn air and soaked every tent, vehicle, and soldier. They couldn't miss even one soldier, or all would be lost. Most of the troops didn't seem to know what to do and ran around in circles with gas in their eyes. The odor invaded their lungs. Some of the petrol floated on the water of the swamp and spread quickly. One man saw the truck coming and ran out waving his arms and yelling for them to stop. Jumping onto the running board, he opened the door and tried to crawl inside. Sam shot him at point blank range, leaving him hanging part way out of the door, his feet dangling on the running board. When Sam swerved to miss a truck parked along the side of the road, the body fell out onto the gravel and was run over by the rear duals. It was covered with gasoline.

Sam knew he had to start the truck's engine. They began to slow down and they needed to move as fast as the spray would let them. They had to hose down the entire camp. They had the upper hand, but that could change if they didn't act quickly. Joe didn't want to miss anyone. Everyone would pay. They were going to get what they had coming to them.

Sam turned the key to the 'On' position and let out the clutch. The big V-8 roared to life like a huge, fire-breathing dragon. The echo of that 454 Jimmy, with no muffler, blasted through the quiet of the early morning darkness like thunder. It was almost deafening, but it didn't seem to bother Sam at all. They thought they were dead men, so he gunned the big engine over and over again. The noise seemed to confuse the enemy even more. They ran out of their tents to see what the ruckus was all about and were hit in the face with gallons of high test. Jamming the truck into second gear, Sam drove through the camp like a madman. It wasn't so much bravery as foolhardiness. They just didn't care. They did the job much better and faster than they could have hoped and made sure that everyone got his fair share of gasoline.

Sam, like the rest, had already given up the idea that he might live through this thing, and had decided to go out in a blaze of glory. He was laughing like a kid at the circus. He gleefully yelled something in Spanish.

Joe yelled to Ben. "What's he saying?"

"He say he never drive before," Ben answered. "He likes it."

"Well, tell him that he can drive for me anytime," Joe laughed.

Some of the more sober Cuban soldiers came out to see what was happening and ran for their weapons. They didn't have a chance. Joe drenched them with fuel and now it was time to light a match.

The choking fumes of the gasoline filled their lungs and burned their eyes as they ran around in a frenzy of mass confusion. They dare not shoot at the truck for fear of touching off an explosion so they shouted and fired into the air. Too late they realized what Joe had intended all along. They tried to run away, but had nowhere to go. The entire area reeked of fuel. The gas truck still had about half of its cargo on board and was bearing down on the fire. Someone managed to get a jeep started about five hundred feet ahead of them and came roaring down the road to meet them in a game of Chicken. They were trying to stop them from reaching the campfire. Sam, who had never driven before, didn't know the rules of the game and slammed into the jeep head on. He pushed it back down the road toward the fire. Joe gave them their Saturday night bath. They did get off a couple of shots into the windshield, but their aim was off and they didn't scare Sam. He kept the gas pedal to the floor and headed straight for the campfire. The entire camp was saturated with Sunoco 260 and they had only about fifty feet to go. It looked as if they would reach their objective. They would go out in a blaze of glory.

Joe wanted to roast Miguel. He learned back in the swamp that you kill a snake by cutting off its head. He wanted to stop this killing machine. He had to take out their leader. If Miguel survived, he would quickly gather another gang of criminals and introduce a reign of terror the likes of which had not been seen in Cuba. Without stopping Miguel, this would be an empty victory. Joe knew Miguel lived in the command tent, the last one on the right. He didn't spray the fuel into that tent, but did pump a couple of hundred gallons into the air and let it rain down all around the tent in a circle. Miguel had no place to hide and no place to run. Joe made Louise a promise at her grave and now he planned to keep his word. Some people would consider them heroes. Joe didn't feel like a hero. He felt like a man committing suicide. He felt terrified.

They expected the tanker to erupt in a huge ball of flame and they would get killed, but it didn't blow. Sam stopped just short of the fire, set the hand brake, and dismounted. Joe was ready to vacate when another jeep came roaring up from behind them, spraying rounds from a 30-caliber machine gun. Joe ignored the hail of bullets and hosed them down with gas. The jeep swerved to the left and hit a stack of ammo boxes. Joe swung the nozzle around and the spray reached the campfire. It blew! Everything went up in a huge fireball.

The jeep was engulfed in flames and its occupants were screaming and waving their arms. One of the men jumped from the burning vehicle and ran into the swamp, perhaps hoping that the water would quench the flames. But even the swamp ignited into a sweeping field of flame. The resulting firestorm swept through the camp like a ravenous wolf, devouring everything in its path.

Joe and Sam hit the ground running. Ben had already started up the slope and was giving them covering fire support, although it wasn't needed. The soldiers were trying to escape the blazing fuel and paid no attention to them. Secondary explosions began to burst from every corner of the camp. Stashes of ammo and fuel tanks erupted like claps of thunder, and sent flaming debris flying in all directions.

"Sargento, would not this be a good time to leave?" Ben yelled.

They bolted up the steep slope, away from the blazing inferno.

The searing heat scorched their clothing and blistered their skin, but miraculously they were alive. They had beaten the odds. The men ran a safe distance away.

As they turned to look back at the camp, Joe said, "This must be what Hell looks like." They watched as hundreds of men ran in total fear and anguish, the flames swirling around their bodies making them human torches. Their screams filled the air. Joe wanted them to pay for what they had done to Louise, Gabby, and the others.

Sam and Ben began to shoot some of the burning villains.

"Save your ammo!" Joe yelled. "Let them get a taste of Hell. That's where they are going." Everything seemed to be ablaze except the gasoline truck and the corner of the camp where the command tent stood. Disappointment stabbed at Joe when he realized that Miguel might escape.

"Shoot the tanker!" Joe shouted. "We need to get that no good killer."

They fired almost all of the ammo they had into the truck and though it leaked like a sieve, to their amazement, it did not explode.

"Aim for the saddle tanks on the truck," he told them.

The first tracer went through the truck's fuel tank and shattered the air with a tremendous blast that rocked the countryside and sent parts of the tank truck flying for miles. The blast knocked Joe and the other men to the ground. They lost their hearing for a while. When the fireball lifted and the smoke began to drift away, they looked at the spot where the command tent had stood. They saw Miguel rolling on the ground with flames surrounding him, his cigar clenched tightly in his teeth. He momentarily stood up and shook his fist at them as the flames engulfed him.

"Are you sure that was Miguel?" asked Carlos, when he joined the small group on the hill.

"That was him," Joe said. "I would recognize that arrogant monster anywhere." Joe voiced a few choice expletives as he watched Miguel burn.

"His own mother would not recognize him now." Ben watched the horrific sight, crossing himself.

Charred bodies lay everywhere and the smell of burning rubber and burnt flesh mingled, filling the air. They heard men screaming and crying out for help. Some of them were begging to be shot. Joe refused their last request and allowed them to suffer. Somehow, their agony made up for Louise's pain.

"Let them feel what it's like being in pain and not being able to do anything about it."

The glow from that fire lit up the whole swamp bright as day. The odor of death permeated the air and smoke ascended about a thousand feet. They stayed until the last cry ceased, enjoying their victory. Then they walked away. They still had one more task to finish before they could leave the area. They needed to dispose of the bodies of their fallen comrades. They couldn't bury them, but they had to see to it that none of them could be identified. Using four 5-gallon cans of gasoline that they had taken from the truck before they had started their run, they doused the bodies with fuel and set them ablaze so no one could take reprisals against any family member of the slain rebels.

The night was coming to an end and soon the sun would take its place in the heavens.

CHAPTER TWENTY

"What a night!" Joe said. "I want to thank all of you! I couldn't have pulled this off alone."

"No, Sargento. It is we who should be thanking you," said Marco. "We ran away like frightened children, but you have made men of us once again." The man held his head high with pride. The others nodded in agreement.

"We have done all we can here. You are released from duty. You can make your way home now, but I don't think that I will ever get back to mine," Joe said. "There's no reason why you should stay."

Sam and Ben stared at each other for a long moment before Ben said; "We will get you home, Sargento. The others can go, but we can't go away and leave you stranded here. You stand out like an elephant with that blond hair. We're going to take care of you. You'll get back to your home."

"How do you intend to do that?" Joe looked skeptical.

Ben brightened, as he came up with an idea. "We'll borrow a boat. We will get you back to the United States."

Joe's heart pounded. He wanted to go home. He was tired and he felt homesick. He wanted to see his parents and his friends. He wanted to get away from this place and away from all the horrible memories. He knew it would be impossible for them to get him home. "You mean steal a boat, don't you?" Joe asked

Ben nodded, a wide grin showing on his face.

"You know very well that isn't possible." Joe said.

"What we just did was also impossible. No? But we did it, didn't we?"

"Yes, I guess we did." Joe smiled at their exuberance.

Even as he spoke, the sky split with the scream of an air to ground missile, followed by an earthshaking blast. Three US navy jets came streaking overhead making one pass after another, strafing and fire-bombing Castro's troops as they came down the road from Playa Larga.

Joe and his friends fell on their faces and covered their heads with their arms as the first of many explosions shook the ground. One by one they came flying by, then went roaring back into the starless early morning sky, each firing into the smoke and flames of the convoy. The troops on the ground returned their fire, but the planes darted away safely. It looked like the jets had done the damage to the camp so Joe and his men were free to leave without fear of pursuit. The planes had covered their tracks with that raid and eliminated any resistance that they might have encountered. No one would be looking for Joe and his little band of rebels. This was more than they could have hoped for. They felt sure this was the help that Bristol had promised, but it was too little, too late.

"This is only the first wave," Joe warned. "Keep your heads down."

They watched in silence as the jets made one last pass, then zoomed off into the rising sun and disappeared. The jets didn't come back and no others followed in their wake. Joe expected another raid and he had the men take cover and lie low most of the day. He kept anxiously watching the sky for reinforcements.

"We must face it, Sargento. They are not coming back for us." Ben stood up and adjusted his gun. "We must go."

"Yes...I suppose you're right," Joe said. "I'd hoped that they'd send a helicopter for us."

Some of Castro's troops came along and began to clear the road of burned out trucks, jeeps, and other debris, so they could pass. They filled in some of the craters left by the rockets and graded the surface smooth with a bulldozer. They didn't even examine the still smoldering corpses that lay scattered about.

Joe's little army didn't want the NAC to know that any of the exiles were still alive so they left for a more secluded place. The spot where the supplies were hidden was the most likely place to rest and decide what course of action to take. They didn't want to fight their way out and with the sergeant's fair skin and blond hair, he would be hard to conceal. They knew it and he knew it. If the Cuban Army spotted them, they could say they were sugar cane workers trying to find a job, but Joe would never fool anyone. They would even have to keep him hidden from the Cuban populace. Most of the people were so afraid of the army that they might turn them over to stay in good with the Cuban soldiers. They had to keep Joe out of sight.

Sam and Ben went to the nearest town to get food, supplies, and especially medicine for their sergeant's wounds. Medicine would be hardest to locate because small towns didn't even have aspirin. When they returned empty handed, Joe made a decision.

"We might as well get started. If we can find and board a boat, we might make it to the Naval Base, and they have medicine."

Carlos and Marco had kinfolk in the neighborhood, so they said their good-byes and headed for the mountains. The other three went up the coast in search of transportation. Staying as close as he could to the water, Sam kept an eye out for a boat while Joe and Ben kept to the tree line. Joe felt sure that if they could get to that U. S. Base, they would be safe and could find a way home. The US Navy would help them. He didn't doubt it for a minute, but his companions didn't seem to share his enthusiasm.

That night, Sam came back from his search and announced, "I found a boat, and it's just what we'll need for the trip to the base. We'll leave as soon as we get our provisions loaded."

Joe grew impatient when the men insisted on bringing all the water and food they could find. It took a long time to load the boat and he wanted to get going. Surely, they wouldn't need all of these provisions. The US Navy would take care of them when they got to the base. A spark of hope kindled in Joe's heart that he might get home to see his family. He knew it was a long shot, but after what they had been through and the fact that they were alive, he started to believe that anything was possible. Still they couldn't afford to wait much longer.

"If we don't get started soon, it will be daylight." He looked at the provisions they had loaded onto the boat. "Do you think we really need to take all this stuff?"

They ignored him and continued to carry gallon jugs of water aboard; so many that Joe lost count. They scavenged every bit of food they could lay their hands on, which was not a lot. They brought rice and black beans. Joe couldn't understand the method to their madness because there was no way to cook on that small boat. So, why bother?

There was a large fleet in the harbor. Most of the boats were fancy rigs belonging to people friendly to Castro, but the craft that the boys selected was neither fancy nor friendly. If Joe had seen her in the daylight, he might have decided to take his chances at swimming home. However, Ben and Sam seemed confident, undaunted by his objections. They slipped aboard under cover of darkness and shoved off.

They chugged along at two or three knots with Sam at the wheel. Ben explained that Sam had never operated a boat before and wanted to give it a try. He did remarkably well for his first time at the controls.

"Sam, you drive a boat even better then you handle a truck," Joe told him, chuckling at Sam's apparent pleasure at handling the controls. Passing several small fishing boats the boys waved to the skippers as they made for open water. Joe peeked out from under a tarp and marveled at the ease with which they made their escape. He felt elated, almost giddy. They were on their way home and nothing could stop them now. Suddenly he felt as confident as the Cuban exiles. As they ghosted along, the old engine knocked and chattered, puffing oil smoke into the air. Cuban men lined the breakwalls and most had fishing poles. They waved to the crew of the little boat and the lads waved back, enjoying their excursion.

Joe stayed hidden down in the boat. They made it out to open water without further incident and headed for the Navy Base. He knew that if they made it to the base that they would be safe. The Caribbean was vast and they were like a grain of sand floating out on the turbulent waves. He could hear the waves beating rhythmically against the side of the vessel. Splash, splash, splash. The boat sliced through the waves. Joe dozed in the bottom of the boat.

Suddenly, a loud crack of thunder reverberated from the angry black clouds and knives of lightning cut through the ebony sky, waking Joe from a fitful slumber. He jumped up, thinking they were being fired upon. Rain pelted him when he pushed back the tarp. He saw Sam fighting the wheel, trying to keep the boat from capsizing. The boat tossed like a feather in a tornado. Ben stooped, bailing water out of the bottom of the boat, throwing it overboard. The pumps couldn't keep up. Joe found an empty bucket and helped. They kept a steady pace until Joe's arms felt stiff and sore. When the bottom of his rusty bucket collapsed, he threw the piece of junk overboard. The wind whipped and pulled at their rain soaked clothing. Lightning cracked above their heads and Joe was relieved to learn that this was a severe electrical storm and not a hurricane. They took turns bailing until the wind finally died down and the thunderclouds drifted away. They had survived. Joe licked his lips. He tasted salt. They passed around fresh drinking water and washed the salt from their mouths.

Exhausted, Joe lay down under the tarp and drifted in and out of consciousness, dreaming and moaning at the torturous nightmares. He came awake when Ben shook him by the shoulders.

"We are there." Ben smiled and nodded his head.

Joe stood up and shook his head to clear away the nightmares. He looked out over the water. A full moon shone brightly around them, illuminating the water around the tiny craft.

"It is there," Sam pointed, "just around that bend. We had better sit out here until daylight. We don't want any trouble from those guys." Sam cut the engine and waited near the entrance of the navy base. He ran up a white flag. They waited.

Joe felt like he had come home. "Home." The word never sounded better. Maybe now he could put the horror behind him and start to heal. He wondered if that was possible. After what had happened to Louise, he sometimes held his ears to drown out her screams, the ones that echoed in his mind. He had never killed before. Now the images of the burning inferno and the screams of men burning to death haunted his dreams and even his waking moments. Would he ever be the same? He doubted it. Still he was only a short distance from the navy base and he would be home.

As the sun crept over the horizon, Joe got his first real look at the boat. She was about thirty feet long and less then ten feet at the beam. Her planking was sparsely covered with peeling paint and her timbers were rotting and riddled with wormholes. If she had been a car, she would have a rumble seat.

"Of all the boats in the harbor for you to choose from, why did you pick this one?" Joe asked, wondering how they made it to the base in this craft. "Did they pay you to take it?"

Ben smiled. "For two reasons. One was the name, 'Sueño de José', that is, how you say, Joe's dream. It is a good omen, no?"

Joe laughed and said, "I hope so. What was the second reason?"

"She was the only one that had no chain and lock," he said with a wink.

"I think I have a pretty good idea why they didn't bother to lock her up. They probably hoped someone would take her. No matter, we won't have to go much farther in this old tub."

Soon, they would be safely among friends and out of danger. The sun climbed higher in the sky, beginning to dispel the morning chill. Sam started the engine and idled toward the inlet. They could see some activity aboard one of the smaller ships. The boat sped out to greet them. Joe felt safe at last. They waved and smiled at the sailors who crowded the rail.

"Those guys sure look happy to see us," Joe said, a little puzzled at their behavior. "But they don't need all those men. All they need is two men to put a ladder over the side for us. Surely they will honor our white flag,"

"I don't think so," Ben gasped. "They are manning that deck gun." As soon as he got the words out, there was a puff of white smoke, followed by a big boom. When the first shell left the gun tube, Sergeant Joe simply refused to believe it. They were firing at him, an American citizen, and an Airborne Infantryman. The US Navy was firing at them, while under a white flag, too. The first round landed about twenty yards from their port bow and went off with a tremendous blast. Sam cut the engines very quickly, just letting her drift, but it didn't help.

"Maybe if they see my blonde hair," Joe said, "They will know I am an American." He stood up and a bullet whizzed over his head, nearly hitting him. He frantically waved and pointed at his hair.

Ben grabbed him pulling him down as a round of fire hit the water. "You make a big target."

"Get this thing started and back her out of here," Joe ordered, giving Sam a signal he understood. Sam nodded and started the engine.

"I told you so," Ben said. "They aren't going to take us under their wing and treat us well. Didn't I say that?"

"Okay! Okay! You said it," Joe said, angry and confused. "Now get this thing fired up and get us the heck out of here."

Sam grabbed the white flag and began to wave it frantically. They looked back in time to see another puff of smoke. This time it hit the boat. The unexploded shell tore through the hull of the old boat and lodged in her bow, leaving a hole about the size of a dinner plate just above the waterline. The fact that the wood was rotten probably saved their lives. It should have sunk them and could have killed them all. Joe's anger turned to rage. His very own countrymen were shooting at them, and for no good reason. They were no threat to any warship in the fleet.

"Let her sink," Joe suggested. "Then they will have to come out and pick us up."

"No," Ben said, shaking his head adamantly. "I will ride with you on a big truck loaded with gasoline into a fire, but this I will not do." He set his jaw stubbornly. "They shoot first, ask questions later. What makes you think they will not shoot us in the water? We had better get out of range before they shoot again." He spoke in broken, halting English.

"Okay, let's go." Ben and Sam had risked their lives to save their Sargento and Joe owed them. Besides, he thought Ben might be right. The navy was shooting at them. "I don't trust them either."

Backing the boat out was their only option. Going forward only served to bring a ton of water into that large hole in the bow, and even in reverse the waves dumped in quite a bit. When they were out of harm's way, they set about trying to repair the damage by stuffing rags into the hole. They didn't have much to work with. The boat did have two bilge pumps, but they were too small and far too old to have much of an effect. It would take a very large pump to hold its own with the amount of water splashing into the hole. The small pumps kept working and the men moved most of the cargo to the back of the boat and took turns bailing with the old bait bucket, but they all knew they were fighting a losing battle. They could not bail the water out fast enough. The little fishing boat had not been made to fight in a war. They felt as though they had brought a knife to a gunfight. 'Joe's Dream' was turning into Joe's worst nightmare.

Time seemed to stand still as they moved across the water ever so slowly. Even though they were going as fast as that old motor would take them, their progress was woefully lacking. Joe was thankful that the men had the foresight to bring all the food they could find and all those precious gallon jugs of fresh water. The tropical sun would dehydrate them in a very short time. They had been slowly working their way toward the Florida Keys. On the second day, sometime in the late afternoon, Ben looked down at the water and saw a fin about twenty feet from the boat. He casually mentioned it to Sam. "There is a lemon following us."

A novice to the sea, Joe was somewhat slow to understand the significance of the moment. He didn't know a bass from a bullfrog, let alone the oceangoing varieties of marine life.

"It could be a great white," Sam said nervously, anxiously looking out across the water, looking for signs of trouble.

"I wish it would find some other boat to follow," Ben uttered under his breath. He quickly made the sign of the cross and prayed in Spanish.

"What's going on?" Joe questioned. "What's upsetting you guys?"

"That." Ben pointed at the dorsal fin as it cut the surface of the water.

"You're afraid of a dolphin?" Joe asked.

"No, not a dolphin." Ben looked at Joe with eyes full of fear. "It is a shark, a big one."

"Why don't we try to catch it and eat it?" They hadn't eaten all day and Joe's stomach was growling. "Lets see if we can shoot it. We still have a little ammo left for the carbine," Joe said, "It might be good to eat?"

Sam took the little rifle from under the seat where they had hidden it from the eyes of any other sailors who may have come along.

He pulled the bolt back, sliding a round into the chamber, took aim just under the dorsal fin, and fired five times before a damp shell casing caused the gun to jam. The fin quickly disappeared under the water, but they all knew the shark hadn't been hurt bad enough to keep them safe from attack.

"It looks as if it might be the other way around," Ben said. "We'll try to not let him catch and eat us. He can tell that we are in trouble and he is hoping for an easy meal. Maybe he'll go away and let us alone." Ben's lips looked white and the strain on his face made him look older. He studied the water, watching for signs of activity.

They kept bailing, desperately trying to keep their feeble craft afloat. They finally bailed out all of the water except for a small puddle. They had to rest. Their joints and muscles ached and they lay down on the rough planking, so tired they could hardly move. The hot sun and the rocking of the boat soon put them to sleep. The little fishing boat tossed on the waves moving aimlessly through the shark-infested water. A hard bump against the craft woke Ben up and he sprang to his feet. He shouted for the others in Spanish. It brought them both to their feet.

Ben bailed like a wild man, yelling in Spanish. Joe and Sam tried to bail with small cups and finally started throwing things overboard to lighten the load. All of that activity brought the shark in closer. He came up out of the water and they could see the wicked, savage eyes before it went once again beneath the waves. He watched them. He played with them. He patiently waited. With a flip of his mighty tail, he swam under their craft and disappeared.

"He must have grown tired of waiting," Ben said, with a sigh of relief when the shark didn't come back.

The water began to weigh down the bow of the boat and the crippled craft washed back and forth as it rolled with each wave. She was floundering fast and no amount of bailing was going to save her. The waves weren't very high, but she was taking on water and rode very low. The hole was right at the waterline now. Each time she rocked, she got another drink. Before they knew it, she had sunk below the hole and started to slip under the waves.

An explosion rocked the boat. The 'dud' she had been carrying in her bow picked this time to come alive and split the old boat wide open, sending her crew flying into the deep blue sea. They landed with a loud splash. They were hurt and bleeding profusely, an open invitation for the shark to come and dine.

Sam splashed around in the water, making a feeble attempt to swim. Every time he started to sink, he would flail his arms around to keep afloat. He sputtered and swallowed the salty brine. Joe reached out and grabbed hold of his shirt collar, dragging his head up out of the water so he wouldn't drown.

"Come on, Sam. You can make it," he shouted. Sam's weight pulled Joe under the water. "I can't hold you. You'll have to help me." Instead of helping, Sam slumped forward and his head went in the water. Joe pulled him up, turning him around. That is when he saw the massive chest wound. Sam's exposed organs floated on the water and his eyes stared sightlessly ahead. A large pool of blood darkened the water around them. Joe held on to his dead friend for a moment before he gave a hard shove, pushing the body away. "Vaya con Dios, Amigo," Joe said quietly, as a wave carried him off and he disappeared under the water.

Joe quickly swam away from the pool of blood. Suddenly a flurry of activity caused large ripples in the water where Sam's body disappeared. The shark tore at the flesh in a frenzy and Joe knew the creature would return for more. He scanned the turbulent waves.

"Ben, where are you?" he yelled at the top of his voice, turning to look for his other friend.

"Here, Sargento. I am over here." Ben waved, trying hard not to splash and draw attention to himself. The waves' pounding at them and the sound of the explosion still ringing in their ears was making it very hard to hear.

Suddenly, something hit Joe with such force it almost knocked him out. For a moment, he thought the shark had hit him. He thought it was the end. He held up his arms and wiggled his legs and feet. He had all of his limbs. He felt something bump him again and sighed in relief when he saw a large piece of the hull floating behind him. It had broken away from the old boat as she sank and popped to the surface. Joe grabbed hold of the huge chunk of wood and held on.

"Sargento, are you all right?" Ben yelled.

"Yeah, I think so. I have a piece of the boat. Can you swim to me?" The waves slapped against Joe, pulling him away from Ben. Joe kicked his feet and tried to guide the hull toward the head, bobbing up and down on the waves. "Swim, Ben!"

"I'm on my way." When Ben reached the makeshift raft, Joe told him the news about Sam. "I don't think he knew what hit him. He was already dead when I got to him."

"It is good that he went quickly," Ben said, spitting salt water. "He was a good friend and a man of honor. He loved Cuba more then life itself."

"In the short time I knew him, I came to love him like a brother," Joe replied.

"Sargento, you are bleeding. We must get you out of the water. The blood will attract the sharks. I will try and hold the wood steady while you climb onto it."

"We can both get on it."

"No, Sargento. It will not support both of us."

"Then we will take turns on it," Joe told him, after he climbed out of the water collapsing on the hull.

Ben agreed with one stipulation. "If we can get the bleeding stopped, we will do as you say. As long as the blood is there, you must stay on the wood." He held onto the makeshift raft. "Sharks can smell blood for a long way and if they come, we will both die."

Ben stayed in the water and held onto the driftwood. Every so often, he would pull himself up onto the wood long enough to rest for a moment, but it would start to sink under their combined weight causing him to slide into the water again. Joe slipped in and out of consciousness. He faded in and out for a long time. He lost track of time. The sun beat relentlessly down on his fair skin. He dreamed and thrashed around on the driftwood. Once he dreamed of a huge white whale cutting through the waves, bearing down on them. Then he heard the distinctive sound of a horn and he lifted up his head to see what Ben was jabbering about.

He saw a boat cutting through the tossing waves. He recognized the familiar white boat with diagonal stripes and the words 'U S Coast Guard' painted on her side. Through Joe's bloodshot eyes, he could see the number 132 on her bow and Old Glory flying from her mast. She was the most beautiful thing he had ever seen. He hoped he wasn't dreaming.

When he heard the first shot, Joe couldn't believe it. Not again! They were shooting at them, just as the Navy had done. Joe cursed and shook his fist at them. Soon two small boats circled them, firing in their direction. He could see the water spout up when a bullet hit. After all they had been through, he thought it an insult to die like this. He wanted to fight back, but they didn't have anyway to defend themselves. They had survived by sheer tenacity, but now they had run out of options. The helpless feeling frustrated Joe.

Ben pointed to the red blotches in the water around them. Joe leaned on one elbow. That's when he saw the fins in the water, circling closer and closer, moving in for the kill. The men in the boats were shooting at the sharks.

Ben got excited and let go of the driftwood. He took off swimming toward the closest boat. It looked as if he might make it, but just as he reached for the waiting hands of the crewmen, the water erupted. As Ben was lifted almost clear of the surface, a great white shark's jaws clamped onto his left leg.

Ben looked toward Joe, and their eyes met for a split second. Joe could see the pain and fear in the young man's eyes, as that monster fish dragged him below the surface. In less then a minute several other sharks converged on the spot. The swirling water had become red for a long way around the area. Too weak to swim, Joe remained on the driftwood, waiting to be rescued. Losing Sam had been a shock, but to see Ben ripped apart by those ravenous sharks was more then Joe's mind could handle. Too weak to stand, he felt himself being lifted. The next thing he remembered was a bright light shining in his face. He could hear voices, but he couldn't make out what they were saying. The only thing he knew for sure was that they were speaking English.

CHAPTER TWENTY-ONE

He awoke in a small room surrounded by people. All of them seemed to be talking at once. Some men were cleaning his wounds, but all he understood was pain. They were hurting him. He kicked and tried to push them away.

"Get some restraints," a white-gowned doctor ordered. When the orderlies tried to tie Joe, he kicked at them and knocked one man against the wall. The struggle knocked over the tripod holding the intravenous container they had been using to relieve some of the dehydration, ripping the needle out of the vein in his left arm, causing the blood to flow from the needle hole. He thought they were the Cuban soldiers and he was determined not to give them any information that would put his unit in danger.

"No!" he shouted. "Get away from me. I won't tell you anything!" He felt the bed linens with his fingers. It felt cool to the touch, not rusty and hot like his metal hot box. He could stretch out. He wiggled his toes and stretched out to his full height. He stared at the white light, trying to clear his head. *Where am I?* He licked his parched lips. He was so thirsty. Why didn't Louise bring the hose to him? He licked his lips again and realized they were swollen and cracked. Why didn't someone give him a drink? He looked down at his feet and saw his boots had been removed. For some reason that embarrassed him.

"All right, which one of you stole my jump boots?" he shouted, cursing and raving.

"Take it easy, buddy. They're right here." Someone handed him his tattered boots. "Go get Beth. He keeps asking for someone called Louise. A woman's voice might help calm him."

In a few minutes, a nurse scurried into the room. The doctor conferred with the white-capped nurse and they looked his way. "I'll take care of him." The sound of her voice soothed Joe's frazzled mind. She patted him on the hand and smiled. "It will be okay. You're safe now. You're in the hospital and we're here to help you. Now just settle down and let us do our job?"

Joe sank down on the bed and watched her prepare a needle. He felt the sting of the hypodermic as she gave him a shot. He felt like he was floating and wanted to go to sleep. He couldn't go to sleep. He had to stand guard. His men depended on him. He couldn't let anything happen to Louise. He had to see Louise, to make sure she was all right.

"Where is Louise? I want to see her," he said, fighting against the drowsiness that pulled him toward the sweet blissful state where the mind rested and memories were kept at bay. He kept asking for her, upset that he couldn't find her. He knew something terrible had happened to her, but what? He had to get to her. She trusted him. He had to make sure she was safe.

"Louise is all right. She wants us to take care of your wounds. You were out on the water for several days. Just lie still and let us clean you up. You can see her as soon as we are finished," the nurse said in a compassionate tone, as she placed a cool hand on his forehead gently, but firmly, pushing him down on the bunk.

"Just let me see her for a moment. I have to see that she is all right," he moaned.

He didn't trust these strangers. They could be working for Castro, or just as bad, the CIA. He wouldn't go to sleep until they brought him a carbine. "I have to see Louise. I want to make sure she is safe." The injection began to take effect and he drifted off into a drug-induced sleep, waking sometime later just long enough to drink a tall glass of water. He felt the sting of the needle once again and drifted back into a troubled dream world of drugged sleep. Louise kept walking, staying just out of reach. He could see her and knew she needed him, but she kept walking away too fast. He couldn't catch up with her.

Joe woke up somewhere on the south side of the Homestead Air Force Base. He didn't know how he had gotten there. He remembered being at a hospital. He vividly recalled the nurse who cleaned his wounds and gave him his shots and drifting off to sleep. How had he gotten outside? He got up off the ground. Was he on a binge? No. He wasn't drunk. He checked his feet and legs. He had clean, surgical bandages on them. He couldn't have been dreaming or hallucinating. The bandages proved that fact.

He asked pedestrians if they saw who dumped him there. "Did you see anything unusual?" he asked a man on a bicycle.

The young man stopped momentarily to check his chain. "I didn't see anything." The young man mounted the bike and sped away, looking back once when he stopped at a traffic light.

Joe tried to stop cars; horns honked, and automobiles swerved to avoid hitting him. He realized that people probably thought him a raving lunatic. Some of them seemed to be afraid of him. No wonder, he thought, looking down at his rotting uniform, all torn and ragged. The questions he asked must have made him seem like a real nut case. He sat down under a bridge and thought about what he should do. He decided to go to the base. He searched for a long time and finally located the Base Commander's office and tried to report to him.

The C.O. looked at him like he had escaped from a mental institution.

Joe tried to explain. "Look, I want to report on the mission to Cuba. Most of my unit was killed. They killed my interpreter. Please get in touch with Bristol at G-2; he'll know what to do."

The C.O. picked up the phone, dialed a number, spoke with someone he called Carl, and then tried to escort Joe to the door. "Look, I don't know anything about any attack on Cuba." He refused to make out a report. "Look buddy, I don't know what happened to you, but you'll have to find someone who knows something about this {so called} mission. No one has notified my office about any such invasion." He looked at Joe's tattered uniform. "I'll see if I can find you a change of clothing. Maybe I can get you on a cargo plane back to Wright-Patterson Air Force Base in Dayton, Ohio."

He waited in the office while the man went looking for some clean clothes. He sat down. His head was swimming and he ached all over. How had he known where Joe needed to go? For a man who didn't know anything about the mission, he sure had made a lucky guess.

In five minutes, the man returned with a pair of old bellbottom jeans, the kind that sailors wear. Joe took off his rotten uniform and put on the jeans. His legs were so short that he had to cut most of the bell off the bottom to make them fit. He didn't bother to hem them. He just wore them the way they were. The C.O. handed him a dungaree shirt and a pair of work shoes. The clothing looked used, but smelled fresh and clean.

Joe pulled the little flag pin out of his ragged slacks. It was the little flag pin that he had taken out of Louise's dead hand, the one he had given her the first night they met.

"That's government property," the C.O. stated, taking it from his hand. Joe looked surprised.

"That's mine. I bought it," Joe told him. That pin had been paid for with his money and with the blood of an innocent girl, but the man kept it and refused to give it back. It was more than a pin. It was a symbol of a wasted life, in fact, many wasted lives.

"Look, buddy. You are going to have to go. Make sure you hop that plane to Ohio."

Joe shook his head. "I know the army is denying everything, but I can't understand how Stanley could turn on me. He was my best friend and was supposed to help me."

The middle-aged man in the immaculate uniform stopped at the door. "Stanley Kennedy? He was on the Houston, when the ship was sunk."

Joe's shoulders slumped and he looked stricken. He had lost almost all of his men. He had lost Louise, now his best friend.

The man softened. "We think he got off o.k. He might be in Cuba. If he is, they will find him and bring him home. Go on now. You can't do anything more for now...YOU DIDN'T HEAR THAT FROM ME! NOW, GET OUT OF HERE, SOLDIER. GO HOME.... and get a life." Joe left the base commander's office.

Knowing he had a few hours before his flight left for Dayton, he used it trying to find that PFC named Jack, the one who had met him the first time he was here. No one knew him or anything about him. Apparently, he had just disappeared from the face of the earth. Joe couldn't find anyone who knew about the mission. He couldn't even find anyone to whom he could give a report.

He caught the flight back to Ohio, thankful that he wouldn't have to hitch a ride from Florida to his job site near Toledo. He was glad to be alive and back in the USA.

Soon he was in Dayton, Ohio, trying to find a ride back to where he had last worked. Joe thumbed a ride on the Interstate. A trucker stopped his big rig and Joe climbed up into the passenger side.

"Where are you headed, fella?" the heavy man in denim asked Joe, before he shifted gears and the eighteen-wheeler sped down the highway.

"My construction crew is working somewhere near Toledo."

"I'm going that way. I can drop you off. You crippled or something? I noticed you have a hard time walking."

"It's from a war injury I got in action." Joe wasn't going to tell him the whole story because the trucker would think he was crazy. Joe knew what had happened, but there wasn't a record of it. Joe couldn't prove it so he decided to keep his mouth shut.

The trucker nodded, handing Joe a sandwich. "Least I can do for one of ours. I'll take you where you need to go."

Joe thanked him. He ate the sandwich, closed his eyes and slept; glad to be home in the United States again, and grateful to be alive. The kind driver even went some distance out of his way to get Joe as close to the job as he could. Joe happily hobbled the rest of the way on foot. He found the crew he had been working with, which surprised him.

In the construction business, the crews move all of the time, but this was a big job and was taking a long time to complete. He just walked in and went back to work as if he had never been gone. He operated a backhoe and sat most of the time on the job.

Mack took him aside. "How did things go?"

Joe took off his hard hat and wiped his face with his sleeve. "It didn't work out. The mission was a flop. I almost didn't make it back. I got shot. My foot still hurts and my legs are a mess."

Mack slapped him on the back. "I'm glad you made it, buddy. I'm sure Uncle Sam is grateful too."

Joe put his hard hat back on so he could go to work. "Uncle Sam denies that the mission ever took place. I don't think I'll be getting any medals for this one." He thought it best not to go into too much detail. By now, he had learned to protect himself. People might call him crazy. He wouldn't be able to stand being locked away someplace. Not after escaping from the makeshift prison in Cuba.

He found some solace in going home to see his parents. Sometimes he talked to his brother Paul about the mission, but never about Louise. Even his brother had a hard time believing the story. Joe tried to pretend that it never happened, but the nightmares invaded his sleep and he started to drink to forget. He changed. He became sullen, distant, not the happy-go-lucky fellow that his family and friends knew. Guilt consumed him. Louise had given her life for him, but he couldn't save her. He felt like a coward and suffered survivor's guilt. He knew the problem, but he couldn't fix it. He drank more and more. He got a little peace when he was drunk, but it was gone when he sobered up. On his usual Friday night binge, Joe sat in his bedroom at his parent's house drinking until he passed out on the bed. He awoke the next day with a pounding headache. He shuffled into the kitchen to get a cup of coffee.

Renee came into the house carrying a bag of groceries. "Hi, brother. I see you are under the weather again," she said kindly, neglecting to scold him for his drinking. She flashed him a radiant smile and proceeded to put the groceries away.

"What are you so cheerful about?" Joe growled, irritated when she laughed and started to sing a church hymn. She was too bubbly for him. When he said as much, she came over and kissed him on the top of the head.

"Why don't you come to church with me? We are having a guest speaker and I hear he is real interesting. He's an army chaplain and you might want to talk to him."

Joe laughed sarcastically, the sound harsh even to his own ears. "What makes you think I would want to talk to anyone in the army?" That was the last thing he wanted. He was still in the reserves for another year, but after that, he was finished with the army.

"He's a preacher. He serves God and his country, but God comes first. You should go with me tomorrow. Listen to what he has to say. Are you afraid he might say something that will help you?" she asked kindly. "Are you sure you want to get better?"

That made Joe mad. He was about to tell his kid sister off when he saw the tears in her eyes. He knew she wanted him to get well. He knew Renee loved him. He had always known it. He remembered how his baby sister had followed him around with adoring eyes, mimicking his every movement. He wasn't like the other guys. He didn't mind her tagging along. She always made him feel proud. Even now, he couldn't stand to see the disappointment in her sparkling blue eyes when she saw him drinking. He wanted her to respect him, but it was hard when he didn't even respect himself. He knew he disappointed her, so on a whim he agreed to go with her.

Renee's smile lit up her youthful face. She stopped by early the next morning to drive him to the little country church. He felt self-conscious when everyone greeted him and shook his hand. He had never attended church and felt out of place. Once the speaker stood behind the pulpit and started to speak, Joe sat mesmerized, listening, a faint spark of hope kindling deep within him.

"I want to tell you about a Man sent on a covert mission to save people from a diabolical enemy. That enemy is ruthless and he is a murderer."

Joe sat up on his seat. His heart pounded. He listened.

"The man left his homeland and his estate. He left His Father. This Man was sent to help the downtrodden, the hopeless caught in the chains of the enemy. The people were in bondage and needed to be set free. The Man was on a mission."

Joe nodded. He understood being sent on a mission. He, too, had been on a mission. He left his home and his family. He tried to free the Cuban people from Castro. The plan failed. However, this was not about him. It was about someone else. Who was this Man? What was His mission? Joe felt it imperative to find out.

The speaker went on. "The man didn't use conventional weapons. He laid down His own attributes. He trusted God. He had to depend on other people for supplies. Widows fed Him. At the end His friends deserted Him and He was tortured and killed."

Joe's heart sank. He wanted to know this Man and now he would never have a chance to meet Him.

The Chaplain smiled. "But death could not hold Him. The enemy thought he had destroyed the mission. Blackness covered the earth. Yet three days later, God raised this Man from the dead and He returned to His followers. You see, the enemy thought he had destroyed the mission, but actually the mission was a complete success."

Joe could hardly believe his ears. How could this be? Who was th' Man? He was killed and God raised Him back to life?

"That man was Jesus Christ, the Son of God. He was sent fro heaven on a mission to save men's souls. Mankind was bound by si but Christ came to set them free. Jesus died, but He is alive and He the Commander-in-Chief of a large army. There is a war going on at th moment. The forces of Satan are attacking the children of God. Th mission is still ongoing." The chaplain paused for a moment. "God i looking for a few good men, women, and children to join His forces. He will never leave you to fight the battle alone. You have a Commander-in-Chief who will never turn His back on you. He will never deny the mission. He has promised victory to those who join Him. Will you be the one to deny His mission? Or will you confess Jesus and become a follower of Christ? Decide today to join the Lord's army. He has a great retirement plan."

Everyone laughed and Joe smiled. The organist started to play a hymn, and the speaker invited the people to come forward to accept Christ. Joe rose at the invitation, walked down the aisle, and knelt at the altar. He prayed earnestly for the first time in his life.

"Please God, lift this burden from me and give me a little peace."

When the speaker knelt to pray with him, Joe asked, "Can God forgive me? I sent a lot of men to Hell?" He explained about burning the camp.

"King David was a man of war. Yet, he was a man after God's own heart. God will forgive you. In His army, you'll have to trade in your gun for a Bible. The Bible is more powerful than the sword. The sword has the ability to change men's actions from the outside, but the Bible has the power to change men on the inside."

So Joe traded in his carbine for a Bible with gold edging. That night he slept till dawn without any nightmares. It was the first good night's sleep that he had had in a long time. He started attending church and learned more about being a Christian. He was in the Lord's army. Now he helped to save lives instead of taking them. He had peace, and it was wonderful.

THE END

EPILOGUE

Re-living this nightmare has not been easy for this old soldier, but it had to be done.

The Parsonage is usually a warm and cozy place. On this sleepless night however, the light glows just a little too bright. Oh, for a little sleep, a little slumber, a little folding of the hands in sleep, to sleep and not dream, but sleep does not come without a price, a high, high price. The solitude is unbearable, yet no one can give him comfort. The night has become an impersonal barracks, where men wait to wage war. The battleground is ever before him. There is no one he can confide in, no one who would understand, or even believe his story about a covert war, fought by a few brave souls, in and for the freedom of Cuba. The year was 1961, so many years ago, yet the faces of his men are as real today as they were then. The Place was Playa Giron, or as it is better known, the Bay of Pigs. There is an ever-present memory of that blistering hot, confining, oil-drenched prison, made of two steel drums, welded together end to end. Even after all these years, the odor of diesel fuel will sometimes trigger a momentary panic, and he can hear the cries of a young girl, as she is beaten, tortured, and raped and finally murdered. She gave her life in an attempt to set her people free, but her dream of a better life was snatched away by cruel men.

She died a horrible death before she had a chance to experience life. She never wanted much, just a chance to live without fear and want. Was that too much to ask?

These memories should have been forgotten long ago, but with the setting sun, they come calling like an unwelcome guest. Night after night, the images return to torment, and rob him of his sleep and peace of mind. There is no escaping, for they are branded on his very soul.

The cries of his fellow prisoners, as they were beaten, maimed and killed, echo in his ears, and will not be silenced.

The pain of old wounds and their scars have faded with the passing years, but the ravaged spirit can find no rest. He yearns for closure, but there seems to be no end. The past is stamped indelibly on his mind; and when he goes to sleep, it all comes rushing back to yank and pull, and to torment. On awakening, it is always the same. As long as he lives in this body, he will hear the outcries against the injustices done, not only by the enemy, but by the betrayal and indifference of the leaders of his Nation. Just as they did with the Polish Freedom Fighters, they made promises they never intended to keep.

These are not the ravings of a madman, but the facts, as history will bear them out. Neither are they a political statement, or pronouncements from some aloof pulpit, but a reminder of a dark time, when truth was sadly lacking, and honor was at a premium.

Now, this has been the real story of "The Bay of Pigs" incident, as it really happened.

Memorial to Marcia M. Cardona

You were only seventeen years old and your life had just begun,
When you saw your people's freedoms disappearing, one by one.
You worked as my interpreter; we had a tyrant to de-throne,
I could tell you thought other human lives were more precious then your own.
You could have taken cover, but you refused to run away,
Although you knew the danger, you made up your mind to stay.
Our captors raped and beat you. Still you would not divulge our plan;
Your cruel death saved the life of a military man.
He was forced to watch your torment; he was forced to see you die.
You died like a good soldier, just as brave as any man,
With a tiny U. S. flag award clutched ever so tightly in your hand.
You would think he could forget it for it happened so long ago,
But your strength lives in my memory, for I was that NCO.

Now as a final tribute, I would like to place some flowers on your grave.
Greater love has no one than this that she lay down her life for her people, and
her country. Now may God bless you, and good-bye my friend.

About the Author

Pastor Joe H. Hill resides in a small town in Eastern Ohio, He is a retired member of the US Army, and has served in both combatant and non-combatant rolls. He is a humble man of modest means, who seldom seeks the limelight, but tends to put others first. It was not always so, for in his younger days he would rather fight then forgive. He was a hard drinking, two fisted, chain smoking heavy equipment operator, for a small construction company. His income was barely enough to eke out a living and pay his bar bill.

When he was approached by an Agent of the Federal Government, and offered a commission, he jumped at the chance. His covert mission would be to help liberate Cuba, and over throw the dictator, Fidel Castro.

The operation was a complete bust, and left him battered and scared, both physically and emotionally. If there is a kinder, gentler man on planet Earth, I haven't met him.

This book, (Shattered Dreams), is his story. I have read it and found that it runs the full gambit of emotions from Humor to Horror, and Romance to Revenge. One cannot read this true account, and not get caught up in its drama.

—*James J. Wears*

Turning Back the Pages of Time

*Turning back the pages of time I look
back and what do I see,
A hope a dream a life that just wasn't
meant to be,
But still your memories come flooding
back across the sea,
some fill my heart with glee,*

*As I look at the ocean with its deep
shades of gray and blue,
I just can't help but think of you,
I think about a love little kiss,
I do hope you know how much you are
missed,*

*Oh how my arms ache to hold you once
again,
Just like they did back when it all
began,
I'm sure you know that in my heart you
never ceased to be,
And oh what a difference that makes to me,
as I sit and stare out across the sea,*

*If you're looking down from above,
you know of my undying love.*

Joe Hill—Author

CAMP BRECKINRIDGE
Home of the Famous 101st Airborne Division

Situated on gently rolling terrain in western Kentucky within a few miles of the Ohio River is Camp Breckinridge, an entirely modern Army Post, designed primarily for training infantrymen.

It is named in honor of General John Cabell Breckinridge, American soldier and political leader born near Lexington, Kentucky, of Scotch-Irish ancestry, who at 35 became the youngest vice president in history of the United States. During the trying years preceding the Civil War, this handsome Blue Grass statesman presided over the Senate with conspicious impartiality. Caught in the Civil War turmoil, General Breckinridge backed the Confederacy and became one of the South's ablest commanders. He went to Cuba at conclusion of the war and thence to Europe. He returned to the United States in 868, resuming law practice and helping develop railroads.

Plans for Camp Breckinridge were outlined at Washington, D.C., in August 1941. First actual construction work was started in February 1942 and in September 15,000 troops, composing the 98th Division had moved in. The Camp area as first established contained 31,000 acres with 6,400 acres being added before the end of 1942. Roughly it covers 58 square miles.

Many army units have trained here. Some of them were, in addition to the 98th Division, the 92nd, the 93rd, and 75th Divisions. After the cessation of hostilities the 35th Division occupied the post for de-activation. There was little activity at the camp from February 1946 until August 1948, at which time the 101st Airborne Division came to Breckinridge. The camp was closed in May 1949 and remained so until reopened in July of 1950. On August 1950, the 101st Airborne Division was re-activated with Brid. General C.E. Ryan as Commanding General.

The Camp contains 10 chapels where services are conducted for all denominations, a post library, 5 air-conditioned theaters, 3 spacious service clubs, several post exchanges and a giant filed house in which it is possible to play four basketball games simultaneously.

Main roads of the camp are macadamized and extended east-west and north-east-southwest in conforming to the general layout of the Camp in its half-horseshoe pattern. Firing ranges for training in all basic infantry weapons lie in the the eastern part of the reservation.

Nearest large cities are Henderson, Kentucky and Evansville, Indiana, 24 and 32 miles northeast respectively. Civilian organizations and the Red Cross of these cities and smaller communities near the post provide extensive entertainment and welfare facilities for the soldiers.

Bus lines provide the chief means of transportation for Camp Breckinridge soldiers journeying to local towns in this picturesque section of the nation.